Taylor &
Chreist

Then Saint Germaine
is a real life
Cinderella

When it is time
you will read and
be transfered
Aloha Nui
Tutu Medeiros

GERMAINE:
Requiem of A
Soul

GERMAINE:
Requiem of A
Soul

The True Story of Cinderella

Andrew St-James

OUR LADY'S TEARS PRODUCTIONS LLC

Published by Our Lady's Tears Productions, LLC
PO Box 5194| Mankato, Minnesota, 56002 USA
www.ourladystears.com Our Lady's Tears Productions is committed to excellence in the publishing industry.

Cover illustration copyright © 2017 by Bogdan Maksimovik. All rights reserved. *Cover design and layout by Creative Publishing Book Design*

Published in the United States of America

ISBN: 978-1-64007-881-9
1. Religion / Christianity / Saints & Sainthood
2. Religion / Christianity / Catholic
16.12.12

CONTENTS

INTRODUCTION

The story of Cinderella has been told, some say, since first-century Greece, but most believe that the version we have all come to enjoy as children was written by Charles Perrault in 1697, under the title "Cendrillon," a story in *Histoires ou contes du temps passé*. Cendrillon, or, as we know her in English, Cinderella, has a difficult and tortuous life plagued with abuse, but, through the power of magic, is delivered from the grip of her wicked stepmother and stepsisters. A tragic if not a hopeless story in which the belief in magic becomes the precondition for escaping the hardships and tragedies of life. At some point, however, many transition to a mind-set where make-believe stories no longer excite their intellect or imagination. Then what? Indeed, the tragedy surrounding the fable of Cinderella is that her story conveys, in the end, that there is no hope awaiting us, for we all do eventually learn to disbelieve in magic. In reading our wondrous fantasy books, we do occasionally pause, if not but for a moment, and wish secretly that fairy godmothers did exist.

Alas, we eventually embrace a more pragmatic understanding of life, and finally let go of the false hopes conveyed by these enchanting fables. How is it that we have become so vulnerable to such fantasies? The calamity is that we have let our children down as parents, because we failed to cultivate their belief in the supernatural. We did not whisper the sweet stories of angels, and refused to nurture in them any kind of mystical life. And so we robbed them, as it were, of a deep and rich interior life; for indeed suffering is not overcome through magic, never has and never will be, yet suffering is part of our lives right from the beginning.

It is sad that our culture does not aspire to recount stories, rooted in truth, rather than fables, that convey comfort to the suffering. There are plenty of fables from which we can take solace, albeit for a brief moment, but nothing really remains. We all have to grow up some day and face life's tragedies one by one as they are thrown at us. We never really do fall back on the fable of Cinderella to provide us with the true comfort the soul needs when times become gray and cold.

There is hope, however, because the true story of Cinderella, though many tend to flee from accurately recounting the chronicles of her life—the abuses, at times, too difficult to bear—is nevertheless a real and hopeful beacon of light for those courageous enough to persevere through the entirety of the pages that convey her wretched life.

In writing this story, the author consulted Jean-Pierre Jouffreau, the archivist of the diocese of Toulouse in France, for the official historical facts surrounding the life of Germaine Cousin. He also referred to the 1904 publication written by Louis and François Veuillot on the life of Germaine Cousin. Make no mistake, the story you are about to read is real, and the main events of her life have been verified and confirmed. The author did, however, take artistic license in filling in the gaps in her life for which there were no accurate records, so that a seamless story of her life could be told. Nevertheless, the reader can rely on the historicity of Germaine's life story and feel confident that the hope conveyed in these pages can be justifiably recounted to others who seek joy and reassurance that they are not alone, and that their suffering is not in vain.

PROLOGUE

The true story of Cinderella began with the birth of Germaine Cousin around 1579 in the small town of Pibrac, just barely twenty-four kilometers west of Toulouse, nestled away in the French countryside. It was a small town, and all came to know about the mysteries surrounding this humble shepherdess.

Germaine was born with a limp arm, and suffered from scrofula, which is an infection of the lymph nodes of the neck that develops into bluish-purple abscesses that often leak. These nontuberculous sores were horrifying to look at, but were not contagious. Known as the *king's evil*, even the Anglican Church's Book of Common Prayer, in 1633, contained ceremonies meant to ward off the evil malevolent spirits many thought were conduits of the disease. Also, by the sixteenth century, the plague was still periodically sweeping through Europe, claiming many lives. It is in this context that little Germaine began her life.

1

Mystery Beneath the Flagstone

*Blessed be the God and Father of our Lord Jesus Christ,
who according to his great mercy hath regenerated us unto
a living hope, by the resurrection of Jesus Christ from the
dead, unto an inheritance incorruptible, and undefiled,
and that can not fade.*

—1 Peter 1:3–4 (Douay-Rheims Bible)

The bereaved family and friends, carrying the casket containing the remains of Madame Edualde Endoualle, solemnly processed, under a gray sky, in the direction of St. Mary Magdalene Church, where they intended to inter her body. Father Sounilhac led the procession, reading out loud the prayers for the dead. In the church, the pallbearers placed the wooden coffin atop the flagstone floor in front of the altar.

Meanwhile, the processing parishioners gathered in the pews. It was only the dignitaries and those who gained civic notoriety who were favored for a burial in the church. None of the regular townspeople could ever hope to be buried there, let alone in proximity to the sanctuary; it was a place normally reserved for the gentry, the clergy, and the saints. The peasantry and the common folk, by contrast, were interred in the cemetery, adjacent to the church. Of course, everyone knew that Edualde Endoualle was not a saint. Although she was known for many acts of charity, everyone surmised that it was specifically her husband's money, his many tithes to the church, in addition to his renown and power within the inner circle of Pibrac's privileged society that got her that coveted space in front of the pulpit. It was the summer of 1644, and more than forty years since a body had been buried in the floor of the church, for few, it seemed, were worthy of such a fine honor. While the congregation quietly filled the pews of the church, Jacques Endoualle, sitting at the front, bowed his head gently and wept. The mayor and the councilman, sitting in seats designated for the dignitaries, postured themselves for visibility—their stations in life having dictated their right to have such privileged seating. The priest and the altar boys processed in the direction of the altar for the high funeral mass.

Monsieur le Curé celebrated the mass in the most solemn manner, and finally, it was time for the homily. Father Sounilhac had been pastor at St. Mary Magdalene's church for several years, and had a good understanding of the spiritual and physical needs of his parishioners. He somberly processed to the ambo, where he stood erect before clearing his throat. He then began to speak of the virtues of a saintly life. Looking out at the faithful, his noble face became pensive as he began to extol the virtues of simplicity and humility, inviting the congregation to emulate the saints in their lives, encouraging them to die to their own desires, and to allow the Lord's sanctifying grace to purify them. He commented on Edualde Endoualle's life:

"Edualde was tireless and selfless in her charitable work for those in need. May the Lord grant her eternal rest; may He say to her: *Welcome into my kingdom, good and faithful servant.* Dear brothers and sisters in Christ, begin now to pray for her soul that she may be liberated from the purifying flames that our Lord has said all must pass through so that our debt may be repaid in full. Saint Matthew tells us that the Lord spoke clearly when he said: *Amen, I say to thee, thou shalt not go out from thence till thou repay the last farthing.* Do not forget this most charitable act…to pray for the dead. Again from the book of Maccabees: *It is a holy and wholesome thought to pray for the dead, that they may be loosed from sin.* Brothers, only through the holy sacrifice of the mass, prayers, and almsgiving, can we liberate these poor souls who can no longer pray for themselves. Pray to our Lord also for those who have fallen away from the Church. Let us pray…"

Father Sounilhac continued after a brief reflective pause. "Faithful Shepherd, you are not a hireling who runs away at the sight of danger, but your fidelity was tested and proved on the wood of the cross. Accept the gift of our gratitude for your marvelous care. Help us to hear and follow your voice. Watchful

Shepherd, who protects the flock and searches tirelessly for those who wander from the fold, retrieve the lost, and bring them home so that you may tend their wounds; O Good Shepherd, who lays down His life for His sheep, nourish your people with the Bread of Life, that we may reflect your likeness, and enjoy the spring of Living Water that never ends. We ask this through Christ Jesus, our Lord—Amen."

After communion, the priest gave the blessing, and the faithful quietly left the church. Traditionally, only close family members would take part in a burial inside the church. Monsieur le Curé closed the church doors, and joined Monsieur le Vicaire, the pallbearers, Jacques Endoualle, Monsieur le Maire, Edualde Endoualle's sister, a few other relatives, Monsieur de Beauregard and his wife, he was a prominent business man of Pibrac, and the two workmen responsible for the physical interment of the coffin. The workmen began removing the flagstone and digging into the earth beneath the stone floor where the coffin was to be placed. As the two workmen, Guillaume Cassé and Gaillard Baron, generally assigned the task of digging graves throughout the parish, buried their picks into the dirt, they unexpectedly hit something. Guillaume yelled out cautiously, "There is something down there!"

Jacques Endoualle, impatient that the interment would take longer than needed, abruptly erupted, "Monsieur! What do you mean by what is down there? Perhaps you struck a piece of stone? Just dig it out, for goodness' sake."

Family and relatives began to gather around the coffin, their peering eyes and faces distinctly concerned and curious.

Guillaume continued, "It is not stone, but rather, it feels like wood."

Monsieur de Beauregard, a nobleman of Pibrac, known for his personal wealth and generous tithing to the church, blurted out, "Another coffin, perhaps?"

Jacques Endoualle, now becoming furious that the plot he had paid for several years ago was already taken, gasped with disbelief. "Impossible! We were told this space was available, and a sizeable donation was made to secure it."

Jacques Endoualle looked to the workman, Guillaume Cassé, with a glacial stare so formidable that Guillaume immediately cast his eyes downward. Even the pastor, who could be heard in the background discussing the matter with the vicaire, was silenced. Then with a controlled voice, his anger visibly contained, he directed the workman: "Keep digging." He was potentially minutes away from an irrepressible outburst.

The other workman, Gaillard Baron, took another swing and buried his pickax deep into a wooden platform. He exclaimed, "It's stuck. I have most definitely hit wood, monsieur."

Jacques Endoualle, reeling in anger, and no longer able to contain the frustration and humiliation of having been sold an already occupied grave, commanded:

"Well, dig it up; pull it out. Do whatever is necessary." Gaillard Baron, having never encountered this kind of difficulty while burying the dead, was now resigned to quietly acknowledging and executing the directives, no matter how unbelievable or mysterious his findings were.

The workman proceeded to free the pick from the wood it was imbedded in. He then moved away the dirt, a shovelful at a time, eventually revealing a wooden coffin. He shouted to Father Sounilhac, "Mon père! It's a coffin!"

Both workmen dusted the surface off; there was chatter among the funeral party. Father Sounilhac, witnessing the coffin enclosed under the floor, was now forced to acknowledge the problem.

"I cannot begin to understand why a coffin would be buried here! There must be a mistake! I assure you, Monsieur Endoualle, I had no knowledge of this…I will certainly find another place in which to relocate these remains. The spot is yours as was agreed," Sounilhac reassured the bereaved husband.

The workmen, having removed all the dirt, lifted the coffin's lid to reveal the body of a young maiden in her twenties, who was completely preserved from any kind of physical corruption. A murmur moved through the crowd as the funeral party looked upon the perfectly preserved body, her arms folded, holding a little candle in one hand, and a garland of fresh carnations mixed with blades of rye in the other. Her face was peaceful, as though she were simply asleep.

Guillaume Cassé let escape from his mouth, "Dear God in heaven!"

"Who is she?" chimed in François de Beauregard, who was also near the coffin.

Kneeling beside the uncovered body, Father Sounilhac, his face and eyes frozen in astonishment, slowly lifted his head, all wisdom and understanding having left him.

"I can't say for sure who she is, but I can find out from the church's registry. I will look into it tomorrow."

One of the pallbearers, upon seeing the incorrupt corpse, ran out of the church in amazement, yelling hysterically through the streets to draw the village people back to the church to see the miracle: "They have found a body in the floor of the church which has not decomposed. Why, it's a miracle! It's a miracle I tell you."

A large crowd began to gather in Pibrac's town center upon hearing the news of the mysterious find, and began to move swiftly in the direction of the church. Meanwhile, back inside St. Mary Magdalene Church, Father Sounilhac, still kneeling beside the coffin, examined the corpse more closely.

"Look! There! On the side of her nose," exclaimed Father Sounilhac, "there is blood, fresh blood." As if gasping for air, he then continued: "Why, that cannot be!"

Marie de Clément Gras, the wife of François de Beauregard, visibly alarmed and troubled by the discovery, whispered with an inaudible punctuated gasp, "Impossible! She can only be a ghost, a…a…a devil."

Gaillard Baron, still in shock over the mysterious discovery, recognized the source of the injury to the maiden's nose.

"It's where my pick went through the wood. I must have grazed her nose," admitted Gaillard. "But how could there be blood? She's been dead for years."

Jacques Endoualle, no longer angry or impatient, admitted the inevitable: "It's a miracle!"

Marie de Clément Gras had a more pragmatic view of the whole situation: "Why, it's repulsive," she exclaimed with disgust, her mouth and eyes clearly revealing that she didn't buy the miraculous explanation. She was a lot more of a pragmatist and realist, and saw a corpse that needed to be reburied, and quickly.

Parishioners peered through the door of the church, wanting to witness the phenomenon. Father Sounilhac, seeing the faithful and the faithless flowing into the church with a ruckus, ran in their direction , imploring them to be silent and to leave immediately.

"Do not enter the church! Go back to your homes, for there is nothing to see here. The sacred rite of interment is still in progress, and so you must leave! I beseech you for love of the soul we are now surrendering to God."

He certainly did not want the curiosity and imagination of the crowd giving way to preposterous notions that they had found a ghost in the sanctuary. But already, the word of a miracle was circulating like wildfire through the town. As he attempted to sway the crowd from the sanctuary and divert it in the direction of the door of the church, he encountered Madame Jeanne Salères, an elderly woman of some repute in the town, and Pierre Paillès an older man, both of them in their eighties.

"Let me see her. I want to see her, Father," shouted the elderly woman.

"Madame Salères, *non*…there is nothing to see," sternly protested Father Sounilhac, who now was fearful things were getting out of hand. He turned away from the older couple toward those around the coffin in front of the sanctuary and called out very clear instructions, "We must keep this quiet until I speak to the bishop."

Jeanne Salères and Pierre Paillès both became insistent that the priest let them see the miracle.

"But we want to see the miracle, monsieur le curé. We both insist."

Father Sounilhac struggled to contain his impatience.

"Madame Salères, I adjure you to not go any farther. All of you leave the church now. We are burying Madame Endoualle's remains, and I insist that this be done in a dignified manner."

Salères continued: "Show us the miracle, Father; that is all we ask. Then we will all return to our homes."

Again, Père Sounilhac attempted to take on a more authoritarian demeanor.

"Madame Salères, Monsieur Paillès, I insist again that you both return to your homes."

Père Sounilhac turned to the crowd, now much greater in size and animated, in an attempt to dissuade as many as he could from their pursuit. He became distracted by one young man who pushed ahead in order to reach the sanctuary area. Père Sounilhac attempted to hold him back, but meanwhile, Jeanne Salères and Pierre Paillès, no longer the center of Père Sounilhac's attention, walked unnoticed directly to the pulpit. There, both gazed at the incorrupt maiden; Jeanne's mouth now wide open, and her eyes bewildered by what she witnessed in the floor, gasped, "Oh my! It is her," she whispered as she turned in disbelief and looked directly at Pierre Paillès.

Père Sounilhac rushed to the sanctuary when he noticed the two octogenarians looking at the preserved maiden, whose clothes, though darkened by the soil, had also not rotted. He was flustered both by their disobedience to his order and their lack of respect for the dead. As he ran toward them, he overheard Jeanne Salères recognizing the identity of the deceased maiden.

"You know her, madame? Who is she?"

Lifting her head in acknowledgement, Jeanne Salères, her voice silenced by emotion, quietly whispered:

"Yes. This is the shepherdess Germaine Cousin. She died more than forty years ago. Let me see…Ah yes! it was in 1601… yes! I remember…it was forty-three years ago. Oh! Look at her now. She is as beautiful as the day she died. This is impossible, unless she be a saint."

The next day, in the Church Council Office, Father Sounilhac stood at the head of a large table surrounded by the members of St. Mary Magdalene's Church Council. He had the parish's burial registry in his hands. The other men listened attentively.

"Gentlemen, the registry confirms it. The girl was buried there forty-three years ago, and there is not a single trace of decomposition on her body, her clothing, or on the flowers she was holding. There was a mix-up in the floor location of her remains, but it is a certainty that this young maiden's body was perfectly and mysteriously preserved."

The vicaire, who in the ancient Catholic right was the assistant pastor, responded with the enthusiasm expected of a novice clergyman, not quite familiar with all of the Catholic Church's rigorous procedures regulating mystical phenomenon. "She must have lived a holy life…we could be looking at the remains of a saint. Surely this is an extraordinary event."

Father Sounilhac, wiping his brow with a handkerchief pulled out of his sleeve, his face contorted and grimacing at the notion of a miracle, promptly corrected the vicaire.

"We mustn't be too hasty in suggesting miracles or sainthood, Father. The next step is to send word of what we have found to the archbishop, Monsignor Pierre de Marca of the diocese of Toulouse. He will likely set up a commission to investigate this matter, that is, if he finds it worthy of consideration."

One of the councilmen, Monsieur Paul de Beauchemin, a prominent merchant of Pibrac and the father of fifteen children, scrupulously listened to the report, and then, as if to appear judicious in his thinking, added, "Is it not protocol to first do an investigation and gather some facts about the girl and her family before burdening the archbishop with such a case? I mean, do we even know her name?"

Sounilhac replied decisively, "Monsieur, I have already taken these steps, and what I have learned convinces me this case is indeed worthy of being submitted to the bishop's office. What I was able to uncover reveals that the body is that of Germaine Cousin, who was born, here in Pibrac, in 1579. She lived with her mother, Marie LaRoche, and father, Laurent Cousin, until 1584, when her mother died from what appeared to be the plague. In reviewing the details of her life that were compiled by many witnesses and filed in the presbytery's office, I tell you gentlemen, this young shepherdess's life is both mysterious and full of paradoxes."

2

Even the Pure Will Suffer

*"It is only the God who is love who can bring light to the
dark secret of human sorrow."*

—Caryll Houselander, 1954 British
mystic and spiritual teacher

This was a period of history ravaged by reoccurring
famines, plagues, and ongoing civil wars between
Catholic and Protestant factions which lasted from 1562 to
1598. Historically named the "French Wars of Religion," it
was a time of nocturnal terror and internal strife that brought
France to the edge of insolvency. It all began with the Protestant
Reformation, initiated by Martin Luther in 1517. Protestantism
spread rapidly through France, gradually shedding its Lutheran
coat to embrace more of a Calvinist doctrine. By 1536, the

Calvinist teachings that the Church was not necessary for salvation, and that all human souls are predestined, was quickly recognized as heretical. The Calvinist followers were referred to as "Huguenots." Despite a Catholic resistance to contain the heresy, Calvinism continued to spread through the 16th century, and by 1555, the first Huguenot church was founded in Paris. In 1570, Pope Pius V excommunicated Queen Elizabeth I (1558–1603) for continuing the efforts begun by her father, King Henry the VIII, of separating the English Church from the Roman Church, and for mercilessly persecuting the Roman Catholics in Britain. In France, things were about to get much worse. In 1589, King Henry III remained childless, leaving no heir to the throne after his death, except for a cousin, Henry King of Navarre, who was the head of the Huguenot cause in France. The Catholic faith was waning, and so it seemed that the Lord found this time of apostasy, war, low morals, heresy, and hopelessness, to be most fitting to plant his little twig, so fragile, docile, and pliant to God's will, in order that she, like a fruitful tree, may grow to bear much fruit.

Hidden away in the outskirts of the small French village of Pibrac, was the little tenanted domain of Mestre Laurens. It is there, among the rolling hillsides of the Haute-Garonnes, that the story of Germaine Cousin began, which became the inspiration for the fable of Cinderella.

The prosperous three-acre farm of Pierre Cousin lay nestled less than 1.5 kilometers east of La Bouconne forest, and 2.5 kilometers west of the little town of Pibrac. He was a respected tailor and held the office of mayor of Pibrac for several years.

His wealth permitted him to purchase the little farm, which he intended to leave to his son Laurent when he became of age. Unfortunately, his son was unskilled in managing financial affairs, and so not long after receiving his inheritance, the farm fell on hard times; extremes in seasonal weather patterns were decimating the farm's yields of potatoes, turnips, and parsnips. And so by necessity he also became a sheep herder. Marie LaRoche was an elegant twenty-seven-year-old devoted housewife of Monsieur Laurent Cousin, and the loving mother of little Germaine Cousin, an only child, now four years of age. Germaine had unsightly sores on her neck caused by scrofula, a nontuberculous infection of the lymph nodes of the neck that was quite unsightly. She also had a lame right arm and hand that bent strangely at the wrist. She was otherwise a pretty child with a pleasant disposition. The mother taught her frequently about God and His saints, and oh! How Germaine loved to hear these stories. However, one Sunday morning, in the early spring of 1583, life's sweetness changed to bitterness for Germaine. Marie was sitting with Germaine on her lap, reassuring her about God's love for her despite her perceived limitations. "Germaine, your life is a gift from God, who knew you before the beginning of the world. O Germaine, your life is so precious to our Lord; He loves you so much that it cannot be measured."

The little four-year-old Germaine, her sweet eyes gazing wondrously at her mother, replied with hesitation, "O maman! Does He love me even with sores? I am so ugly and I frighten other children. Don't I frighten God too?"

"Germaine, the Lord loves all of you," Marie LaRoche replied with tenderness, as she visibly became touched by her daughter's innocent concerns. She gently continued, "Everything you think is ugly, God loves, because He sees what the world cannot."

Still not content that Jesus loves everything about her, Germaine continued, "But, maman, does God even love my crooked arm and hand that do not work very well?"

Marie replied, "Germaine, the Lord especially loves that arm of yours."

"Why, maman, does He love my arm? It is so useless," answered Germaine, insistent.

Collecting herself for moment, Marie closed her eyes and raised her face to heaven, as if to seek some divine whisper. She gently responded, "Monsieur le Curé tells us that the Lord uses weakness to mystify or confuse the wise and unsettle the learned. Through this weakness, God the Father is glorified." Marie paused for a moment as she thought through the message she wanted to leave with her little daughter. A gentle smile lit up her face as she suddenly understood the response she needed to give. "Germaine," she said reassuringly, "God's ways are not the world's ways. He can bring good and strength out of what is dark and weak."

Her mother paused a moment and pulled out a handkerchief from the sleeve of her dress, bringing it to her mouth just in time to cover her cough. As she pulled the handkerchief away, she could see a small amount of blood; quickly, she hid it in the side pocket of her apron and continued talking with Germaine.

"Love God with all of your heart, your mind, and your soul despite all you have suffered; trust in Him who knows everything and then Jesus will approach you when you least expect it. He does this because He understands your needs before you do. Like a good father, He will guide you, Germaine."

Several days later, Marie LaRoche's health declined noticeably. She began finding it difficult to keep up with her daily workload. Her breathing was labored as she stirred a pot of lentils hanging over the fireplace. Wiping her brow with the back of her hand, she struggled to find the energy to finish meal preparations. Finally, she walked to the door to call Germaine into the house for dinner.

"Germaine! Germaine…come, my child. It's time to eat! The soup is ready."

Germaine entered the house joyfully and immediately put on an apron in order to help her maman with dinner. She could sense that her mother was struggling and needed some assistance. She ran promptly to set the plates and bowls on the table for her papa. The workmen only shared breakfast and lunch with them; they went home to their families for dinner.

Suddenly, the door opened and Laurent Cousin entered. Worn out from the day's work in the field, he sat on the chair in front of the blazing fireplace. Germaine ran to her papa. Tired and grumpy, his face grimaced as he saw his unsightly daughter run in his direction.

"Ah! you little nit, let me be," he blurted out. "Go away, I am worn out and tired."

He dismissed Germaine with a wave of his hand, indicating with a disgusted face that he was not interested in any displays of affection.

Laurent never did come around to accepting his daughter's deformities. The large abscesses erupting from her neck disgusted him, and her lame hand and arm was a constant reminder of the miserable life that awaited him and Marie as they grew older. All he could see was a girl that would be a useless burden in the house as well as on the land. It was not a blessing, it is certain, for a farmer and sheep herder to have weak and sickly children. Laurent had hoped for strong boys that could eventually help him with the farm work. But to no avail; his prayers went unanswered. Instead, God gave him an abomination, a burden that weighed him down, someone to be ridiculed and laughed at. *What an embarrassment*, he thought to himself.

"Go and help your maman!" Laurent grumbled.

"Oui, Papa!" Germaine uttered, an air of melancholy ever so slightly tainting her joy. She resigned herself to the notion that her papa would never love her. She then ran to her maman to seek solace and to assist her. Marie noticed the brush-off from the corner of her eye, but refrained from saying anything. She knew how Laurent disliked Germaine; secretly, she held on to the hope that his heart would someday change. So, to deflect the noticeable snub by her husband, Marie quickly inquired, "Laurent! How was the work?"

"The day was long, and I'm glad to be home," he answered with a sigh.

Marie stepped in the direction of Laurent and, removing his hat, kissed him. Laurent stood up from the chair and walked in the direction of the fireplace to warm his hands.

"Come, mon chéri," Marie said to her husband with a warm voice, "dinner is ready."

She walked over to the counter in the back of the room and began to prepare bowls of lentils for Laurent, Germaine, and herself; she portioned out, as well, the next day's lunches for the hired hands. Laurent untied and removed his boots. Germaine helped her maman serve the lentils, and once the table was ready, she and her maman sat down.

"Laurent, dinner is ready…," Marie called out with a little hint of frustration in her voice. Laurent got up and sat at the head of the table.

"Merci, ma chérie," Laurent softly said with a long-drawn sigh, as if the burdens of the day had suddenly come to rest on his head. He picked up the wooden spoon and began to slurp the soup.

"We must give thanksgiving to our Lord for the food," Marie quickly interjected at her husband's irreverent conduct.

"Ah! yes…I'm sorry," he quickly replied, as if coming out of a mental stupor. He promptly clutched his hands together and bowed his head, closed his eyes, and recited the blessing. "Bless us, our Lord, and these thy gifts, which we are about to receive from thy bounty through Christ our Lord. Amen."

Germaine, wooden spoon in hand, looked down at the plate of lentils in front of her, and began to eat with avidity. Laurent immediately began to slurp and grunt as if he hadn't eaten in a week. Marie, her eyes fixed on her daughter and husband as they ate, reflected a deep sadness, which nobody really noticed. Her face, pasty and white, revealed the effects of the illness that had been eroding, for some time now, her very will to live. Suddenly, Germaine, about to fill another spoon with lentils, looked up at her mother, and seeing that she hadn't yet taken a bite, said: "Maman, are you not hungry?"

Marie shook her head, putting her hands up to her face to cover her mouth.

"Marie, you must try to eat something," Laurent exclaimed. "The doctor insists that you eat so that you may keep your strength."

"I'm not hungry," Marie responded. "I just don't seem to be able to swallow anything." Laurent looked at his wife with concerned eyes. She stared back at her husband, her eyes weary and fearful. To distract him from her condition, she promptly inquired about the sheep herd.

"Were you able to sell the lambs today, Laurent? Did you get some money for the household? We need flour for bread, you know. I'm uncertain if I will be able to stretch our food reserves any further, Laurent! It is getting hard!"

"Yes, I sold the lambs, but not at the price I was hoping for. Monsieur Le Boyer is a difficult man, and I'm never able to get fair market price with him. I try, but he controls the market prices so well that I can't even go elsewhere for a better sale. So here!" He placed the pitiable earnings on the table with a sigh. "That should help somewhat," he uttered, his voice fading. He stood up and walked in the direction of the fireplace to warm himself. The night was going to be cold.

Marie, aware of the darkness brought on by their financial struggles, appealed to Laurent's religious beliefs; that is, what little there was left. "We should say the rosary, Laurent. We need our Lady's help," she suggested to her husband.

As Laurent stared out the window with a pensive and troubled look, he responded, "Yes…Yes…We should do that…I'm not sure why? She gives us no visible assistance in our troubles."

"Laurent!" Marie gasped with concern and shock in her voice. "Speak not of our Lady in this way, especially in front of Germaine." She placed her hands over Germaine's ears to shield the child from the scandalous comment.

With a weary monotone voice, Laurent acknowledged his shortcoming, "Yes…Yes…You are right. I am sorry."

Laurent lifted Germaine from the chair and placed her on the floor in front of a statue of Mary. Looking down at her, he sarcastically said, "Germaine! Pray to Mary…pray for help!"

Marie knelt beside Germaine and began reciting the rosary. Laurent walked in the direction of the window and there remained standing with a preoccupied face, his eyes scrutinizing the horizon, wondering if it was all worth it, this praying.

Three nights later, Marie, lying on her bed, appeared pale and weak. Laurent knelt next to her. Germaine stood against the far wall of the room, looking on, frightened and not fully able to absorb the chaos unfolding before her. The doctor diligently worked at keeping Marie's fever down by cooling her burning forehead with water. Madame Mélançon, their trusted neighbor, stood by the doctor, immersing rags in cold water and handing them to him.

Laurent, kneeling by Marie, reassured her as she coughed. "It's all right, my dear. The doctor is working hard. You'll be better soon." Marie's sickly eyes looked back at Laurent with concern.

"Please call for Monsieur le Vicaire," Marie whispered weakly, as if it were her last breath.

Doctor Baillet gently placed his hand over Laurent's shoulder to comfort him, and then said, "The end is near, Laurent. Go and get Monsieur le Vicaire so that he may administer the last rites."

The two men stared at each other for what seemed like an eternity.

"I will," replied Laurent, "I will leave immediately."

Doctor Baillet added, "Perhaps it would be best if you take the child with you, monsieur. I have much to do, and there is so little time."

Laurent immediately turned to madame Mélançon and said, "I will take her and leave her at the church as I pass by to get Monsieur le Vicaire. Monsieur le Curé is saying mass today, so I will tell him that you will take Germaine home afterward."

"Of course, monsieur Cousin, I will take care of it," madame Mélançon replied with assurance.

Laurent walked over to Germaine, her back still leaning against the wall, her eyes evermore alarmed and teary.

"Come with me, little one."

Laurent lifted Germaine up in his arms, and began to walk to the door in haste.

"Papa, where are we going?" Germaine asked with distress.

"We are going to get Father Guillaume at the church in Pibrac. He's going to pray for maman."

Marie began to weep as Laurent walked in the direction of the door with Germaine wiggling in his arms; as Laurent left the room, he gently closed the door. Doctor Baillet continued to wipe madame Cousin's forehead with a wet cloth as she coughed up blood.

Father Guillaume Carrière was the assistant pastor at St. Mary Magdalene Church. He was assigned to assist Father Jean-Granet Sablières, right after completing seminary in Toulouse. Enthusiastic and gentle, Father Guillaume loved the priesthood. He wanted nothing more than to bestow blessings on his parishioners. Every occasion was favorable for a blessing from Father Guillaume. The people loved him tenderly.

A small crowd was entering the church as Germaine and Laurent stood outside next to the horse and carriage.

"I must go help your mother, Germaine. Madame Mélançon will come and get you after mass is over."

Germaine nodded, her face stoic and determined. The church was the ideal place for her in this time of crisis. She was resolved to pray to the Lord Jesus for her dear maman. Ask anything of the Lord, and He will grant it, she had been taught by her dear maman, many times. Now she had an unfettering resolve to throw herself at the feet of Jesus.

Back at the house, Laurent stood just outside the door, his hand trembling as he tried to light his pipe. Once it was lit, he smoked it with great urgency. As he exhaled the smoke, he looked up to the sky and muttered to heaven an inaudible supplication for mercy.

After a moment, the doctor stepped outside. He placed his hand on Laurent's shoulder, shocking him out of his prayer.

"Laurent, the end is near. Come, the priest is preparing for the anointing. We will pray together."

Laurent slowly emptied his pipe on the railing of the porch before putting it in his pocket. He fixed his hair and walked into the house with Dr. Baillet.

Marie was almost completely out of breath. Pale and delusional, sweat was streaming down her forehead. She wheezed and coughed with every shallow breath she took. Madame Mélançon held a cold compress to her forehead and wiped the blood that kept flowing from her mouth. The priest was preparing to hear madame Cousin's confession.

Laurent went in the corner of the room, allowing the priest to calmly listen to Marie's sins. Madame Mélançon moved away from the bed and positioned herself near the door, beside Laurent.

The priest heard her confession and anointed her with oil. Then he provided viaticum.

Meanwhile, back at the church, Father Jean-Granet Sabrières was standing at the altar; he turned in the direction of the congregation and said, "Benedícat te in nomine Patris, et Filii, et Spiritus sancti; amen." Once the final blessing was given, he processed into the sacristy with the altar boys to remove his vestments before returning to the church's pews, where he normally prayed after mass.

As mass concluded and the people filed out of church, Germaine remained praying in a pew near the front. Madame Mélançon entered and walked in the direction of Father Sabrières, who was kneeling in one of the back pews. As Germaine prayed, Madame Mélançon and Father Sabrières conversed with each other with voices too soft to hear.

Father Sabrières slowly got up and walked in the direction of Germaine. Meanwhile, Germaine, kneeling in the pew, prayed fervently, remembering her mother's counsel to always love Jesus no matter how difficult life became.

"My Lord and my God, I love thee. Please, my Jesus, listen to my poor prayer for maman; she is so sick and suffers so much. Have mercy on her and on her soul, take pity on maman and give me strength, I beseech you. If she dies, I'm not sure how papa and I will manage...but I trust, my Lord, that you will provide for us. Even if you take mama from me and papa, I will still love you, Lord, with all of my heart. Amen."

Germaine bowed her head in between her clutched hands and wept, the rosary beads intertwined between her fingers. The child, still deep in prayer, was unaware that the parishioners had since filed out of the church to return to their businesses and shops. Father Sabrières's hand gently touched her shoulder and startled her into sudden awareness. Turning her head promptly and looking around confused and alarmed, she realized that it was Father Sabrières who had surprised her.

"My child," began Father Sabrières, with some hesitancy in his voice, "I have something very important to tell you. Germaine, your dear mother has passed away. My child, pray to God for your mother's soul. Commend her; commend her soul into the loving hands of Almighty God. Come, my child, I will take you to Madame Mélançon, and she will take you home."

Unable to fully comprehend and absorb the full impact of the priest's news, she blurted out, "Oh, my poor maman!" and began, distraught by the news, to weep deeply.

Outside, the rain began to fall heavily, and the overcast sky appeared to reach far into the horizon. It was as if darkness had come to extend its disquieting grip on the region. Obscurity of day settled on the people of Pibrac.

The details of the funeral were quickly made. There, in the misty rain, the muddy soil, and the dreariness of an early spring day, stood Germaine, her left hand tightly grasping her father's soaking coat, her eyes fixated on the open grave with the closed wooden coffin inside. The Mélançons and some villagers reverently stood by the grave, everyone mourning for the loss of Marie LaRoche, while Father Sabrières conducted the burial rites. Germaine let go of her father's coat, seeking his reassuring grip. But, alas, Laurent's hand, tightly tucked away inside his coat, would not grasp Germaine's hand to comfort her in her sorrows.

3

Wedding Oneself to Suffering

God instructs the heart not by means and ideas, but by pains and contradictions.

—Fr. Jean Pierre de Caussade, SJ, 1751

Madame Belchères moved swiftly down the path in the direction of the Cousin home, her right hand holding a leather sack that was embroidered with daffodils. It was a bit of an irony since Ragonde Belchères did not exude any kind of hope or joy normally attributed to springtime flowers; rather, her sad disposition reflected more of the darkness of winter and the gray tones of death. Plainly, she was a sturdy woman who was level-headed, stern, and walked with purpose, for indeed a sense a mission clearly defined her.

Arriving at the front door, she placed her sack on the ground, straightened her collar and hat, and knocked. Laurent opened the door. "Madame Belchères. Please come in," said Laurent.

Ragonde Belchères's face, worn, old, and grave, looked at Laurent without expression for a moment, before the old spinster walked in, closing the door behind her. Her critical eyes swept through the house, catching every little detail that was not to her liking. Her disapproving eyes then turned to Laurent, who proceeded to welcome her.

"Thank you for coming, madame. I realize it was short notice."

Laurent Cousin could see the woman's harshness and bitterness, but, having nobody else he could rely upon in these difficult times, he resigned himself to making the best with what he had.

"I am pleased to be of service, Monsieur Cousin. The short notice was not a problem for me," replied Ragonde.

Ignoring her reply, he proceeded to clarify the purpose of his trip and the expected time of his return.

"I have to quickly deliver a batch of wool to an acquaintance, as she needs it right away. I planned on sending it with a worker who was headed that way, but his wife became ill. So now I must go to Montpellier myself. While I am there, I will have to manage some other affairs, but I should not be gone for more than two to three weeks."

"We will have plenty to do to keep us busy, monsieur. You need not worry!" Ragonde reassured Laurent.

"If a situation arises, and you need to attend to something, Madame Mélançon is always happy to look after Germaine for a short time."

"I don't foresee the need," replied Ragonde, her voice betraying her visible annoyance at the suggestion that she might need help.

Germaine, looking out the window, remained stoic and uninterested in welcoming the intruder. Laurent turned in the direction of madame Belchères and continued, "In any event, I would like you to meet my daughter. Germaine! Come here," Laurent shouted out with a loud authoritarian voice. As if shaken out of dreamland, Germaine abruptly turned in the direction of her father. "Come here, I tell you," he repeated sternly.

Germaine promptly walked to Laurent's side.

"Germaine, this is Madame Belchères. She's come to take care of you while I travel to Montpellier. I shall be gone no longer than three weeks. She will be keeping the house and making your meals and those of the hired farm workers while I am away; all the things maman used to do," he pointed out with regret still lingering in his eyes.

For a brief moment, sadness took over Germaine's innocent face.

Laurent, turning to Ragonde, continued his instructions. "Germaine will be able to assist you in your work despite her bad arm. Use her as best you can. She is a good girl and will listen to you and do all that you ask of her."

Germaine hesitated for a moment, and then looked into Madame Belchères's threatening eyes, before acknowledging her. "Bonjour, madame," she softly said.

"I also have two workers," Laurent said. "One farms in the field, his name is Pierre Dauvet, and the other is a shepherd named Claude Laudin, who watches over about ten to twenty sheep in Manaut pasture; they will need to be fed only in the mornings and at lunch as they go back to their wives for supper at night."

"Yes…Well, I will do my best, monsieur, to accommodate the needs of your daughter and your workers. I always do my utmost," Ragonde assured Monsieur Cousin.

She put her bag down and began walking around the house, as if she were an inspector general about to review the neatness of some military facility.

She cleared her voice and said, "Now, Monsieur Cousin, I plan on taking my duties here very seriously. Your home will be impeccably clean, and the meals on time. I expect you are deferring to me for matters of discipline, and I demand complete respect and obedience from the child. In short, for the duration of my time here, you can rely completely on my discretion regarding the management of your household. Be assured, Monsieur Cousin, that I will take care of everything."

"I have no doubts, Madame Belchères. I extend to you a warm welcome. Let me show you your room," Laurent suggested.

Upon entering her upstairs quarters, Ragonde placed her bag on the bed and sat next to it. She looked around the room for a moment, and began to promptly unlace the bag.

The first item she took out was a wooden bilboquet, which was a toy consisting of a cup and ball. She held it in her hands and looked at it for a moment, and then placed it on the nightstand. Through the doorway, Germaine was peeking in. She looked with curiosity at the bilboquet. She had never seen anything like it.

What is this thing she pulled out of her bag? Oh my! What a strange ornament, she thought to herself. As Ragonde turned in the direction of the door, Germaine quickly vanished down the stairs to bid her papa farewell.

Laurent, kneeling in front of Germaine, his hands on her shoulders, said to her, "Germaine, just be sure to mind Madame Belchères and help her with the chores. It may take some getting used to the work, but I expect you to be obedient to her. Am I making myself clear?"

"Oui, Papa. I promise," Germaine assured her father.

"Good. Now, I must be on my way," Laurent informed his daughter, his look already distant as he began to contemplate the long road ahead of him. He would be traveling to Toulouse first, and then southeast through Carcassonne, Narbonne, Béziers, and, finally, Montpellier; the distance was around 267 kilometers.

Laurent settled himself into the buggy, ready for the first segment of his trip to Toulouse. As the horse galloped away into the distance, Laurent never waved to his daughter, who stood at the edge of the property, hoping for a final good-bye.

That evening, as Ragonde lifted the top off the cauldron, steam came out in abundance. Germaine, her hands on the table, waited to be served. Ragonde put a wooden spoon in the pot to stir the soup, then suddenly stopped and looked at Germaine. "Germaine," she shouted. "Remove your hands from the table and sit up straight."

Immediately, Germaine removed her hands, swiftly hiding them under the table.

"You will learn your table manners, young lady," warned Ragonde, her sense of mission now becoming clearer.

Germaine, sheepishly looking downward, replied with a submissive voice: "Oui, madame! I am so sorry."

The next day, the late winter sun shone brightly over the little French countryside. Ragonde, kneeling over a washtub, was vigorously rubbing a shirt against a washboard; as she took it out of the tub to show Germaine, who had knelt down next to her, she said, "Now, it's your turn. Do just like I did."

Ragonde took the shirt and walked over to the clothesline. Germaine looked at the washtub for a moment and took another shirt from the tub. She began to scrub it against the washboard with her right hand on top. It was difficult for her, as her right hand was without any dexterity or strength.

Ragonde soon returned to see Germaine struggling with the washing. "You're not scrubbing hard enough. Put some effort into it," shouted Ragonde.

"I'm trying, madame," replied Germaine, her efforts visibly fruitless.

Ragonde approached and knelt next to Germaine, who had stopped washing. She reached down and held up Germaine's right hand, still holding the shirt. She ripped the garment out of the child's hand, paused for a moment as if to get new bearings, then proceeded to place it in Germaine's left hand.

"Use this hand on top," commanded Ragonde. "If you don't apply pressure, the clothes will never be sufficiently clean."

Germaine continued to wash the shirt, this time with her left hand, while Ragonde grabbed more clothes off a pile and placed them into the washtub.

"Be sure to wring them out properly before hanging them out," the housekeeper directed Germaine with sternness and impatience.

Germaine dutifully listened to the elderly mistress, applying herself the best she could. The work helped distract Germaine from the longing she experienced for her mother, whom she missed. Meanwhile, Ragonde went inside to begin cleaning the house.

Nighttime was especially difficult, as it was in the silence of the night that the memories of her maman would flood her mind with overwhelming longings that caused her heart to ache with grief. How she missed her, but she took great solace from a reading she had heard at church just the previous week.

"No trial has come to you but what is human. God is faithful and will not let you be tried beyond your strength."

But oh! How she felt that this suffering was much more than what she could bear. Father Sabrières's preaching that Sunday did, however, help her to understand. She remembered him likening life to a tall mountain with many storms raging at the lower levels, and especially at the base, but with crisp blue skies found at the peak. "Be glad and rejoice," the priest had said, "in knowing that those storms are allowed or divinely ordered by God for our good. We need only trust in Him that he knows what is good for our soul. There, at the summit, is the cross," he had taught, "and it is where there is peace, and it is there, at the foot of the cross, that souls should remain, even though thunderstorms and tempests of all sorts should be raging below." She remembered that Father Sabrières insisted that "We must throw ourselves at the feet of Jesus, when we are scared or sad, trusting that the cross, there at the summit, will shelter us from fiercest winds, the most treacherous gales, should they attempt to overtake the peak. Run to the foot of the cross," he counseled, "where you will find Mary waiting to comfort you, at that place of ignominy. There, in the least likely of places, stillness and peace will be found; it is the way to interior peace." So, he concluded, that it was at the summit that we can be still, very still, and know without a doubt that He is God.

It seemed to Germaine that this longing and aching in her heart were the very storms that Father Sabrières was referring to in his homily. She found that the fury at which these longings assaulted her would subside when she knelt and recited the rosary, using the beads her mother had given her when they said the rosary together. "Oh! Maman, come pray with me to Mary, that she may help me not be so sad," Germaine whispered, as she knelt before the little altar next to her bed.

Bright and early the next morning, Germaine was scrubbing the floor, her left hand holding the scrub brush, her right awkwardly drying the floor with a cloth. Sitting in the big rocking chair knitting, Ragone kept a watchful eye on Germaine, who momentarily paused in her scrubbing to look in her direction for some kind of validation. But nothing; there was no acknowledgment of her efforts.

"That section is clean. You can now wash under the table," directed Ragonde, with staccato-like commands. Germaine diligently applied herself, no longer seeking consolations, affirmations, or approbations. Life, it seemed, had become difficult but still manageable. It was during these moments of emptiness that she began to speak quietly with God, not so much for consolation, for she was learning not to depend on any, but for mere companionship.

That night, tired and exhausted, Germaine knelt before the beautiful little statues of Jesus and Mary that were placed on her little altar tucked away in the corner of her bedroom. There, bathed in gentle moonlight that captured her almost angelic facial features, her eyes closed in meditation, she prayed with tears streaming down her cheeks. Germaine's lips silently uttered what seemed like supplications to heaven. She missed her maman so much, but despite the melancholy, internally she was attempting to climb that mountain to the very summit, seeking that quiet and peace Father Sabrières had spoken about so beautifully. Madame Belchères stared through the crack of the bedroom door left ajar. Seeing Germaine's prayerful demeanor, she called out with a loud, accusatory voice, "Germaine!"

Startled by the severity of Ragonde's strict and disapproving shriek shattering the silence, Germaine turned to face Ragonde, whose presence appeared so imposing.

"Stop your whimpering this instant and go right to bed. There is much to be done tomorrow," Ragonde ordered.

Germaine got right up from the kneeling position and crawled into bed.

The next morning at the crack of daybreak, Germaine was by the well, filling a large pail with water. She turned and struggled to carry the pail back to the house. Once she replenished the house's water reserve, off she went, making the beds with clean sheets. She got to Ragonde's room and placed the sheets on her bed. While looking around the room, her eyes locked on to the bilboquet she had seen several days before on the bedside table. Slowly she walked towards it. Looking around, and seeing no sign of Ragonde, she picked up the toy and began to examine it closely.

Suddenly, the housekeeper opened the door in haste, and seeing Germaine prying through her belongings, became filled with anger.

"Put that down!" Ragonde exploded.

Germaine quickly yet gently placed the bilboquet down on the bedside table and looked at Ragonde Belchères with remorse in her eyes. The mistress walked over to Germaine and took her by the right ear and led her out of the room screaming in pain.

"I'm sorry, madame," Germaine yelled.

"Have you no decency? All I told you to do was put the sheets on my bed, not inspect my room!" yelled Ragonde. She led Germaine to the front door.

"Madame, I am so sorry," Germaine painfully exclaimed.

"You were not been given permission to touch my things!" replied Ragonde, whose sense of privacy was violated. "Have you not learned to respect people's privacy?" she cried out, continuing to lead her outside, her right hand tightly pinching Germaine's ear.

"I'm sorry, madame. I just wanted to look at the toy. It is so…beautiful. I've never seen anything like it before," Germaine explained. Madame Belchères abruptly let go of Germaine's ear, a sad and wistful look reconfigured her face.

"It was not yours to touch!" Ragonde angrily corrected Germaine. A moment of silence passed between the two, as they stared at each other. The mistress suddenly regained her look of anger.

"Go and find me a switch," she ordered Germaine.

"Please, madame, I won't ever touch it again," the young girl reassured.

"I'm going to make sure you don't," the housekeeper venomously promised.

Germaine was facing the fence, her left hand clasping the post as hard as she was able. Behind her stood Ragonde, both hands holding a small branch. She proceeded to vigorously whip Germaine's backside. The little girl whimpered with dread, crying out that she was sorry. Ragonde, hesitating upon hearing the supplications, rekindled her fury and continued striking Germaine until the branch broke.

That evening, the sun had quietly set on the farm, washing in darkness all traces of light. The candles in the house were lit. Germaine and Ragonde sat at the table with food in front of them, and a chilling thick silence permeating the room. Ragonde finally broke the silence. "You are a wicked little girl. I see that being punished was a new experience for you. Let it be a lesson to you, so that you keep your nose out of other people's business," said Ragonde dryly.

Germaine remained quiet, her eyes looking down, listening to the reproaches directed at her.

The following morning, Germaine rose early and began with the washing of shirts in the washtub. A pile of dirty clothes by her side, she endeavored to wash just as Ragonde had instructed her, using the strength of her left hand to compensate for her weak and lame right arm. Afterward, when rinsed, Germaine would hand the clothes to Ragonde, who would examine them closely before taking them to the clothesline. Neither of them spoke a word. The silence was deafening, but yet they continued to work without any chatter throughout the day. It was while they were in the henhouse, collecting eggs, that Germaine saw the sadness in Ragonde's eyes. The two moved quietly from one hen to the next, Germaine, holding a basket in which the old spinster would deposit the eggs gathered from under each hen. Suddenly, Ragonde, her hands holding three eggs, inadvertently dropped them onto the ground, thinking the basket was right next to her. She looked at the broken eggs, her sullen mood now exposed, her eyes tired and weary. Germaine intuitively knew that Ragonde carried pain that, like a river, ran deeply within her soul.

That evening, Ragonde and Germaine were sitting at opposite ends of the table, eating their food in silence. Germaine gathered enough courage to finally speak. "I was wondering, madame, why it is that we don't say grace before meals?"

Unsettled by the innocence of the question, she responded, her voice weak and resonating with bitterness, "I know not God, and He knows me not. I have turned from Him, for He is distant and cold. Some have referred to him as a loving God? Ha! I think not, but one who is vengeful and full of wrath. And so I wish no association with Him."

Germaine's mouth remained opened, surprised by Ragonde's response. How could she reply to her comment and not anger her more than she already had? Out of divinely inspired prudence, she chose not to speak a word. Her eyes looked down in silence.

That night, Germaine knelt down, as she usually did, by her altar, and prayed the rosary; her intentions were for the healing of Ragonde's lack of faith in God, and to be able to leave her own aching heart behind, in the lower levels of the mountain. She had been lost in prayer for hours, struggling to climb to the peak of that mountain, her eyes closed in deep meditation, when the three-o'clock moonlight immersed her in a mystical glow. She was exhorting Jesus to tell her why Madame Belchères was so angry; she expressed deep remorse for her failings that made Ragonde displeased with her. "Oh, my Jesus, I am so sorry. Please let me know how I can be a good girl, pleasing to Madame Belchères and to you." She grabbed the crucifix that was on her altar and passionately held it to her heart, throwing herself at Jesus's feet nailed to the cross. And there, at the feet of the Savior, she cried in sorrow. Then, an internal prompting caught her by surprise and silenced her into an ecstatic state, as she heard Jesus speak to her in an internal locution: *My child, if the world hates you, realize that it hated me first. If you belonged to this world, the world would love its own; but because you do not belong to the world, and I have chosen you out of the world, the world hates you. If they persecuted me, they will also persecute you.*

Ragonde, in her bed, was tossing and turning, unable to sleep. She had already gotten up frequently through the night, filled with worry and dread. She decided to get up again, but this time picked up the bilboquet that was on her night table. Sitting on her bed, holding the wooden toy, tears began to run down her cheeks. Wiping her tears with the back of her hand, she remembered telling her little Henri many times not to get his feet wet. She recalled how he came back that one evening, many years ago, and did not tell her his feet were soaking wet. It started with a cold, and then, within a few days, his cough got worse, and soon he became delirious with a high fever. She remembered the doctor telling her and her husband, Marcel, that Henri would likely not make it. They had the priest anoint Henri; he passed away the next day. She brought her hands to her face in disbelief, while whispering, "He was still so young; why, my God? Why?"

Suddenly, as she opened her eyes, she perceived a strange light coming from outside her room; she thought that perhaps she had left a candle burning. Puzzled by the glimmer, she slowly stood up to investigate. As she cautiously walked down the hallway in the direction of Germaine's bedroom, the light emanating from the cracked-open door became more intense. She cautiously peered through the opening. Inside, the moonlight softly shone on Germaine's face. Ragonde leaned in for a closer look, and saw what looked like a small dove shimmering above the child's head, its wings opened wide. Germaine, kneeling in ecstasy, was bathed in an ethereal glow that was not of this world, unaware of what Ragonde was witnessing. Unexpectedly, Ragonde, overcome by such an overwhelming sense of beauty, purity, and love, immediately fell to her knees, and there, in that posture of extreme humility, bowed her head, unable or unwilling to look at the mystical phenomenon. The mistress then lifted her head again, as if to convince herself she was not seeing things. She wiped the tears from her eyes and again attempted to contemplate the divine light in which Germaine and the dove were bathed, but the dove was no longer visible; only the light remained. She had never seen such beauty in her life. Germaine, coming out of her ecstatic state, remained motionless on her knees for a moment, her eyes darkened by a sadness she was unable to hide. She then slowly got up and crawled into bed; it was four o'clock in the morning.

Germaine's purity and innocence pierced Ragonde deeply, reaching the inscrutable depths of her soul. "How can this be?" Belchères uttered imperceptibly, her entire body exhausted, consumed by what she had witnessed. She remained in the kneeling position, silent and unable to fully comprehend what had taken place. With a strained and almost inaudible voice, she whispered, as if her very breath had been taken away, "My God! Forgive me. This is not possible...it is...miraculous." Ragonde Belchères left the room quickly and began to sob uncontrollably, her conscience convicting her of having lost her faith. Overwhelmed by her guilt, she continued to sob. She perceived, in what seemed like one flash of light, all the times she was neglectful, dishonest, slothful, prideful, and mean-spirited. Her conscience reminded her of an unkept promise she had made to the Lord, while caring for her dying husband, Marcel. She was still a young woman, and the grief she felt at the prospect of losing her husband prompted her to supplicate the Lord for mercy. She had also done the same for her little Henri as he died. Ragonde's face was frozen in astonishment as she relived the moments before their deaths, witnessing her prayer of supplication to the Lord for their lives as she knelt by their bedsides.

She had thought to herself, *He never answered my prayer; the Lord never helped me, my child, or my husband...He abandoned us all in our sorrows.*

That was the moment she had truly lost her faith. She had lost all hope that there was a God. But now, because of the beauty and purity she had witnessed, she could no longer doubt. It seemed as if no bitterness or grief could ever linger in her soul again. Somehow, she knew that her son and husband were with God; she now suddenly understood that her prayers had been answered; the Lord did come and take them from their suffering; mercy had indeed been shown. Now the Lord was still waiting for her to keep that promise she had made of doing penance in reparation for her husband's many offenses. Ragonde, astounded by the revelation, by the clarity of what she was seeing, blurted out with deep sorrow: "My Lord and my God!" And then bowing her head, sobbed at length, allowing her tears of contrition to abundantly flow.

4

Appearances Deceive

"The world must shake the dust of worldly affections and attachments and arise from its sins before it can enjoy seating itself in charity."

—Venerable Louis of Granada, OP,1588

I t was Sunday, March 18th, 1584, when winter's unpleasant grip on the country finally lifted. Spring was in the air, and the people of Pibrac sighed that some relief from the harsh winter had finally arrived. The early signs of spring brought joy to many of the faces that had long ago lost their resilient smiles and bright dispositions, the consequence of the long and biting cold days of winter. Germaine was seated next to Ragonde Belchères in the second pew, up from the sanctuary. Germaine always enjoyed being close to the front where she could see all the priest's detailed ceremonial gestures. Behind them, ten rows back, sat Jean Facet with his wife, Louise, and their three children. He was Pibrac's notary; the son of a wealthy large landowner who wielded some political influence in the region. In front of them, Claire Leguard and her husband, François, were kneeling reverently. They seemed to be reciting the rosary together, although a closer look revealed that it was François doing all the praying; Madame Leguard was clearly distracted. François was a local farmer, and a hardworking man who supported his family well. The congregation's winter attire was lighter; scarf and mittens were either left with the horse and buggy or back at the home.

Father Jean-Granet Sabrières processed into the sanctuary with five altar boys. Mass was particularly long this Sunday, as the homily pertained to charity and self-effacement; he was guiding everyone's penances during the holy season of Lent, in preparation for Easter. Father Jean was trying to point out the importance of doing acts of charity for love of Christ, and not for love of self or for recognition.

"To be self-effaced really means to be invisible to the eyes of others," he explained with a grave voice. "It means to remain hidden in our acts of love and charity, so that only the heavenly Father may know and recompense us in the next world."

It was clear from the many faces staring, as if into emptiness, that few were grasping the depth of the priest's words. The entire congregation, except for the few that did not make it to confession, finally got up and lined the altar railing to receive communion. As Claire Leguard walked back up the center aisle after receiving communion, she turned and looked at Jean Facet, giving him a faint and discreet smile. Her eyes then shamefully looked down to avoid his gaze. It was not apparent to anyone in the church that they were having an affair. François Leguard, however, was very suspicious that his wife was unfaithful, but feared confronting her, especially since they had two daughters, who would most certainly be disturbed by this kind of confrontation.

Monday morning, Jean Facet went to the office particularly early. He had some clients from Lyon who were trying to purchase property on Pibrac's main street. Given the hard times that France was experiencing, this was certainly an unusual business venture to say the least. He also was in charge of organizing the bread distribution for the poor; this was something he committed to every year for the last five years, in order to be prominently positioned for visibility. He had found that working alongside the priests, and sometimes the bishop, tended to pay off in the long run, especially when it came to appointments on strategic town committees that carried some influence.

"Monsieur Vincent, I need to dictate a letter. If you could be so kind as to come this minute," called out Jean from his office.

"Oui, monsieur, I'll be right there," replied Monsieur Vincent. Antoine Vincent was Jean Facet's trusted secretary. He compliantly acquiesced to Jean's order and quickly sat by his desk, pen in hand and ready to dip it into the ink bottle on Jean Facet's desk.

"Yes, well." Jean cleared his throat. "Please address this short letter to the Bishop of Toulouse. Dear Excellency, it is with great pleasure that I announce to you the beginning of the Bread for the Poor campaign which I am organizing with Father Jean-Granet Sabrières, and his vicaires, Father Guillaume Carrière and Jehan Hoguet of St. Mary Magdalene Church in Pibrac. This year's efforts are aimed at widening the distribution throughout the region of Pibrac; in this campaign, we would like to broaden our reach all the way to Launaget, St. Jean, and St. Alban. We are hoping for some financial support to help the bakers of Pibrac produce enough loaves to meet the needs of the many poor. Sign it 'Your faithful servant in Christ, Jean Facet, Notary.'" He then turned in the direction of his secretary. "Thank you, Monsieur Vincent, that will be all." He dismissed him with a wave of his right hand, as if shooing away a fly.

Jean had a sense of fulfillment when organizing the Bread for the Poor campaigns each year. He enjoyed standing out from other citizens by his good works, and he especially took a great deal of pleasure in befriending the priests and bishop through these efforts. It gave him, he thought, a kind of pass to get into heaven. Jean was convinced that he had reasoned out the great mystery of the salvific economy: *Do some good works, go to church, love Jesus, be friends with the priests, and God will forgive any lapses in virtue*, he thought. *He had already died for our sins, hadn't he? So these blunders in human behaviors are truly forgotten, erased from the book of life*, he persisted in thinking. *Thank God for this Protestant Reformation. It has brought such a breath of fresh air into the stuffy old church. This talk of sin by the priests is nonsense, and very destructive.*

Facet now looked intently at the stack of deeds on his desk that he needed to address. They belonged to prominent merchants of Pibrac that were transferring ownership of two properties to the Panse family of Lyon for commercial development. The Panse family was one of the wealthiest family-owned merchant companies in France that traded in spices, leather, and silk products. They had stores in Lyon and Anvers and were looking to expand into Pibrac. The Panse family representative wanted him to finalize reviewing the articles of law to ensure the legal clearance allowing him to proceed with the development plans. After several hours reading carefully the details of the deeds using a dimly lit candle, Jean set the papers down and rubbed his eyes, now tired and weary by all the details. He could not see, in his first review, any problems with the properties or the businesses they intended to administer. Everything looked legal and straightforward. As he was signing several pages and applying the notary seal, he noticed a slight inconsistency in both of the projects. Funds had been borrowed from the Italian Medici Bank in Lyon to upgrade and repair the buildings, but there was no confirmation that repairs had been completed. He sat back on his chair, rubbed his eyes a second time, knowing that the repair bills he was staring at were either errors or downright fraudulent. If he spent the necessary time investigating these anomalies he would be late for his encounter with Claire Leguard, which was scheduled for later that night. Her husband was out of town, so the prospect of fueling this affair further was exciting and of great interest to him. He read over the details of the deeds with a scrutinizing eye, determined to identify the problem, but hoping for minor errors that would necessitate but small adjustments; he did not want to be late for his rendez-vous. The second review revealed more problems and inconsistencies that suggested not errors but what could be considered a misrepresentation of the properties. He understood that this application would require more attention on his part, but now was not the time. He closed the file and placed it on top of the heap of papers and documents on his right. He left the office and drove his horses, in haste, in the direction of the Leguard farm.

As they lay in bed together, Claire turned in the direction of Jean and whispered: "I feel so guilty, Jean, yet I love you so much. What am I to do? I am committing a mortal sin every time I am with you, yet I cannot help but be with you."

"Who cares, Claire? Mortal sins are invented by priests to get parishioners to go to mass and confession. Those priests have such high moral codes that nobody can follow them. Can't you see how happy we are when we are together? In the end, that's all that matters. I can't believe that God does not bless us."

A period of silence remained before Claire replied, as if to divert the conversation away from sin, "Who was the woman with Germaine Cousin today at church? Have you seen her before?"

"No, I haven't," replied Jean, not really interested in talking about the girl.

"She doesn't seem to be from here," continued Claire.

"Laurent hired her as a housemaid. She runs the household for Laurent while he is away in Montpellier," replied Jean, who was more interested in getting his clothes on.

"She seems like a strict woman, maybe even harsh. I fear that poor Germaine will have a tough go of it. She is such a weak and sickly girl," continued Claire, now showing some discontent in seeing Jean get dressed.

"She's an ugly, sick child, a throwaway. She would be pretty useless around the home with her limp arm and hand," said Jean. "Who would want a child like that? I can hardly look at her with her leaking abscesses. She is repulsive."

"You're leaving?" asked Claire reluctantly.

"I have to go home to Louise. When is your husband returning from Saint-Lys?"

"Tomorrow night," replied Claire.

The lovers kissed and Jean inconspicuously left the house, while looking both ways before exiting.

At home, Jean had trained himself to be a skilled liar. It was always coming back from his illicit encounters with Claire that was the most difficult to justify, because Louise would always inquire about why he was so late coming back from the office, or where he had been at such a late hour. All difficult questions to answer without betraying his true whereabouts, intentions, and feelings for his wife! He didn't love her anymore; it wasn't clear to Jean if he ever loved Louise. He had been seeing Claire Leguard now for over three years, whenever secret meeting times could be orchestrated, which amounted to dozens of times per year. Those encounters with Claire were the most exhilarating and passionate he had ever experienced. It was like another part of his soul had never lived until he met Claire Leguard. With her he felt the vitality of life, the excitement of being alive. *"Why would I ever give that up?* he thought to himself.

The next day, Jean Facet was back at his office feverishly reviewing the deeds in preparation for his meeting with the property investors from Lyon, scheduled for that morning. There was, however, a problem, a very big problem; several of the Pibrac landowners were clearly colluding together to misappropriate funds they borrowed from the Medici Bank for upgrading the buildings they intended to sell to the Panse family. It was evident that all but some of the money was diverted instead in the direction of their private businesses and homes, and very little went in the direction of the physical improvements of the buildings they intended to sell. So the problem he had been struggling with boiled down to two items: funds borrowed from the Medici Bank were misappropriated, and the two properties for sale to the Panse family were misrepresented, with the likely intent of illegitimately selling the properties at a higher price. This kind of fraud he encountered occasionally, but a stern slap on the hand usually corrected the situation. This time it was different; two of the landowners wanted to meet with him about one hour prior to meeting with the merchants from Lyon. He suspected that they were going to try to bribe him to sign off on the fraudulent deeds. Normally he would most certainly never acquiesce to any kind of irregular proposal or deal, but times were hard, and extra money would certainly help his financial situation. The incredibly rainy falls, springs, and summers over the last three years, had shortened harvests and ruined many of the crops. This had, inevitably, precipitated the local economy into a less than robust performance. Agriculture was the main driving force of the economy, and when the harvest is not good, all the people of the region struggle; he was certainly no exception.

A bribe during these difficult times is certainly attractive, he thought to himself. *It would normally be out of character for me to even consider such an option, but I have to feed my family*, he rationalized.

Marc Moreau and Rodrigue Paget arrived five minutes early to the meeting.

"Bonjour, Monsieur Facet; good of you to see us prior to our meeting with the Panse family."

"Yes, of course," replied Jean Facet, who was already anticipating the bribe. "Please sit down. How can I be of assistance?"

"Well, Monsieur Facet, Marc and I—I mean, Monsieur Moreau and I, wanted to make sure that the deeds were signed and that everything was in order," replied Rodrigue Paget with a noticeable level of unease in his voice.

"Messieurs Paget and Moreau, there are some irregularities in the deeds, and in the overall sale package you are submitting to the Panse family. Dare I say, gentlemen, that the deeds have a distinct odor of foul! I am afraid that I cannot ethically sign off on such a deal," replied Jean Facet, with something of an uncompromising tone.

"Now, Monsieur Facet, let's not be hasty about this until all the facts are known," interjected Rodrigue Paget, who nervously saw the sale being annulled.

"Yes, indeed, monsieur," piped up Marc Moreau, equally feeling the pressure. "Yes, let us look at this with clear heads. As you well know, the Panse family is one of the wealthiest textile merchant families in Europe and carries a great deal of influence in the economy of Lyon. Their interest in expanding commerce southwest of Lyon is of great benefit to our region, and to Pibrac specifically. This deal, Monsieur Facet, must go through for the sake of the people who need some hope and some prosperity to come their way in such difficult times. This has been our mission, Monsieur Facet, from the very start."

"I don't know what to say," replied Jean Facet. "First, the papers you submitted can be considered fraudulent. I cannot, for the life of me, see where your renovation loan from the Medici Bank actually went. Those buildings have not undergone the planned changes described in the loan proposal. You are misrepresenting the properties, which falsely inflates property sale prices. I understand, also, that you will potentially be making a great deal of money from this transaction, a reality that sullies or, shall we say, discredits your altruistic aim to help the population of Pibrac."

"Now, now! Monsieur Facet. Those renovations are forth coming and will, in the end, comply with the loan guidelines," Marc Moreau quickly and skillfully interjected.

"This is what I propose in order to make good on our project," piped in Rodrigue Paget. "As an incentive to bring this very beneficial deal to a close, we believe that 13 percent of the sale could be our contribution to a very good cause I believe you have been directing in the region. Is it not called the Bread for the Poor campaign?"

"Why, yes, it is!" exclaimed Jean Facet, shocked by the skillful presentation of the bribe. He paused for moment, and then continued. "I would expect that there would have to be an administrative fee for dealing with the ongoing management of the donation as well?" inquired Jean Facet.

"Yes, of course," chimed in Marc Moreau, feeling they had just averted tragedy. "There will indeed be additional funds sent to you specifically for such a purpose."

"Well, then, if I can be assured that property repairs and renovations will proceed prior to the Panse family taking possession of the buildings, I believe our business is done," said Jean Facet.

"It will be taken care of, monsieur, I assure you. I will be sending you tomorrow a letter describing the details of the donation," replied Rodrigue Paget.

"You may want to proceed to the next room for our meeting with the Panse family," directed Jean Facet. "I will join you shortly after I finish signing the deeds and other documentation."

5

God Chooses the Lowly

*"...But the foolish things of the world hath God chosen,
that he may confound the wise; and the weak things of the
world hath God chosen, that he may confound the strong."*

—1 Corinthians 1:27–28 (Douay-Rheims Version)

Germaine woke up, the sun shining through the window
and onto her face. She smiled and offered up her day with
a prayer in the kneeling position. Then she ran down the stairs
to the kitchen, her eyes still a little puffy from her sleep; it was
ten o'clock. Germaine realized she had overslept as she saw the
brightness of the day through the window. Suddenly, she began
to rush, knowing full well that she would be surely beaten for
being late with her chores. She hurried back up to her bedroom
and put on her dress in haste, her facial expression revealing

alarm and sorrow. How could she explain her negligence to Madame Belchères? It was indefensible.

"I thought you were going to sleep all day," responded Ragonde upon seeing Germaine come into the kitchen area. She then turned her attention to the eggs.

"I'm sorry, madame. Why didn't you wake me? We must be hours behind on our chores," Germaine nervously replied.

"No chores today, Germaine. Now wash up, breakfast is almost ready, and then we have things to do in Pibrac."

The excitement and mystery lit up Germaine's face. *What are we going to do in town?* she wondered.

The trip to Pibrac was only a mile and half, so the carriage ride did not take long. Ragonde and Germaine walked through the crowded city square. There were vendors on the street selling their wares. It was all very colorful and bright. Because it was a spring festival, there was a juggler and mimes. Germaine smiled in amazement. Ragonde looked at her with subdued amusement. Next, off they went to the confectionary shop to buy some special jams and fruits. As they exited, Germaine was chewing on a small apple; everything tasted so good.

They kept walking in the direction of the town square. Germaine finished her apple, but still had some on her face. They took a few more steps and Ragonde noticed the apple bits on the side of her mouth. "Come here," she gently called out.

"Did I do something wrong?"Germaine responded with some trepidation. She hesitantly walked in the direction of Ragonde. As Germaine stood before her, the mistress knelt down and wiped off Germaine's face. Ragonde smiled; something she never did. The tension between them had dissipated after the previous evening's experience. Ragonde was trying to make up for the harsh behavior directed at Germaine over the last three weeks. However, Germaine had no understanding of why Ragonde suddenly became kind.

The next morning, Germaine stood patiently while Ragonde brushed her hair.

"Your papa will be arriving today sometime, I suspect, so you must get your hair brushed. I just hope he doesn't arrive too early," Ragonde nervously said. After a while, Ragonde suddenly stopped brushing Germaine's hair as the door suddenly opened; Laurent was standing at the entry, luggage in hand.

"Papa!" Germaine exclaimed with excitement. She rushed up to him and hugged him. Ragonde Belchères paid him no attention but went directly to stir a stew cooking on the fire.

Laurent knelt to face Germaine. Looking right into her eyes, he said, "I have a surprise for you outside."

"A surprise! For me?" Germaine inquired excitedly. Laurent and Germaine walked through the doorway, but Germaine stopped suddenly upon seeing her father's guests. Outside the wagon stood Armande de Rajols and her daughters: Loyse, eleven years old; Anne, nine; and Françoise, who had just turned seven; they were getting out of Laurent's carriage together.

"Germaine, I'd like you to meet your new maman," Laurent casually said, as if "a new maman" was something she had been hoping for. Not quite understanding what was going on, she remained expressionless.

"Come, Germaine," Laurent invited his daughter. "Let's all get acquainted." He led Germaine to Armande and her children. In the doorway, Ragonde Belchères looked on, understanding that her role at the Cousin residence was coming to an end. She knew that she should be moving on by early the next day, if not sooner.

Ragonde's bag lay open on the bed, while Germaine sat next to it, folding clothes. She looked sad. Ragonde gathered her other belongings and placed them on the bed.

"You don't have to help me pack, Germaine. I can manage by myself," Ragonde said with reassurance.

"I don't mind, madame. You have been good to me." Ragonde gently smiled at this little angel. "You have also helped me, child!" replied Ragonde.

Germaine did not understand how she was of any help; she could barely keep up with the laundry.
"But you should really go and spend time with your new family," Ragonde instructed with some authority in her voice.

Germaine paused a moment then hesitantly said, "Can't you stay?" Ragonde stopped packing her bags and looked intently at Germaine, then walked over and knelt down in front of her.
"I wish I could, my child…but it is not to be," Ragonde replied. She bowed her head as if surrendering to God's most

holy will. She continued, "My sister has dear friends in Bordeaux and they need my help. I'm going to look after their home like I did here."

"Things will be so different once you've gone," Germaine, replied as if to make a final case for why she should remain with them.

"Life is about change, Germaine. Think of it this way. You have a new mother," Ragonde reasoned. "This will be a new beginning for you."

Germaine's countenance suddenly darkened at the prospect of having another mother. *Nobody could ever replace my dear maman, who was so gentle and kind*, thought Germaine.

Ragonde tried to reassure and encourage the child: "She seems like a fine woman who will take good care of you and your father. And you will have some playmates as well. They are your sisters, Germaine! You will come to appreciate how important sisters can be."

"But I'll miss you so much," Germaine freely admitted, her heart visibly aching.

"It's best not to think about what you have to lose when you have so much to gain. Now isn't that right?" Ragonde tenderly replied.

"Oui, madame." Germaine conceded.

There was a long pause in the exchange. Ragonde Belchères looked in the direction of the door and then back at Germaine, whose grief was very apparent.

"Now I must go. Your papa is waiting for me in the carriage, to take me to Pibrac. Do you want to come with me for the ride?"

Germaine looked down at the floor, trying desperately to hold back her tears.

"Would you like that?" inquired Ragonde.

"Yes," was all she could utter.

Ragonde and Germaine walked in the direction of the door, each carrying a bag. Armande was down in the kitchen sweeping the floor. She paused a moment as she looked at Ragonde and Germaine.

"So, I assume you have all your belongings?" asked Armande matter-of-factly, revealing her methodical, no-nonsense temperament.

"Yes, I do. If Monsieur Cousin is ready to bring me to Pibrac, I shall get into the wagon. My coach to Bourdeaux arrives this afternoon," Ragonde said with equal dryness.

"Have a safe journey," replied Armande, who could not hide from her face the disdain she had for the old spinster. "Germaine, run and get me some water," Armande suddenly yelled. Her screeching voice disturbed and unsettled Ragonde, who all of sudden became concerned about what kind of a life would be waiting for her new little protégée. Germaine tensed up a little upon hearing her name, and proceeded to look in Ragonde's direction, as if seeking some kind of assistance.

"Actually, Madame Cousin, I've asked Germaine to ride with me into town so we can say proper good-byes. I do hope that is in agreement with you. And I also need some help with my bags."

"I assume you walked here carrying both bags yourself," replied Armande, who was now feeling territorial and possessive.

"Yes, but I've acquired a few belongings during my stay," bounced back Ragonde with agility.

"I see," responded Armande resolutely, no longer wanting to prolong the exchange, fearing that a rather nefarious streak of her character may become evident. A long, icy pause engulfed the room. Outside, the sound of children playing could be heard.

Ragonde finally broke the silence. "I'm sure you can have one of your daughters help you."

"My daughters, madame, are not maids," Armande protested with a strong bitterness resonating in her voice.

There was another long pause as Armande stared at Ragonde with an icy contempt. "When you return, Germaine, I have some chores for you to do," Armande finally instructed.

"She'll be back to do them in no time!" Ragonde reassured the new matriarch.

"Very well," Armande conceded as she went back to sweeping.

A horse-drawn stagecoach entered Pibrac. It was the coach bound for Bordeaux, which came daily at the three o'clock hour. It slowed considerably as it went through the town's streets, in the direction of the town center. Eventually it came to a stop near a bench where Ragonde and Germaine were sitting. Laurent Cousin patiently waited in his buggy. The stagecoach driver sat on the perch, holding onto the reins. He looked at Ragonde Belchères. "Are you headed for Bordeaux?" the coachman yelled.

"Yes, I am," replied Ragonde as she got up from the bench. "Are you departing soon?" she inquired.

"That I am, madame," the stagecoach driver blurted back. "We are leaving in just ten minutes," the driver added as he got off the perch and opened the door. Ragonde Belchères grabbed her bags and stood up. She looked down at Germaine, whose eyes were streaming with tears.

"Get a hold of yourself, Germaine. And if you ever come to Bordeaux, be sure to come and see me," Ragonde said with warmth, as her right hand gently stroked the child's cheek.

Germaine was unable to respond. Ragonde took two steps in the direction of the stagecoach.

"Good-bye!" yelled out Germaine, whose voice was stifled by a fear which suddenly reemerged after being quelled soon after her mother had died. In prayer she had resolved to throw herself at the feet of the Blessed Virgin Mary. She had surrendered to her celestial mother the fears and anxieties that followed in the wake of her mother's death. Now, suddenly they were all surfacing as if monsters from a lagoon. Ragonde turned and smiled at Germaine one last time as she entered the coach. From the door of the stage coach she yelled out, "Good-bye, Germaine!"

The driver closed the door behind her and climbed into the perch. He slapped the reins with vigor and the horses began galloping in haste. Germaine stayed on the bench and watched the stagecoach fade into the horizon.

Meanwhile, back at the Cousin home, Armande was walking through the house. She picked up a cheap vase, examining it with disdain, snorted disapprovingly, and put it back down on the mantle. *What poor-quality dishes*, she thought. As she moved through the rest of the house, she dreadfully concluded that the house was a step down for her and her children. How could she fit into Pibrac society if the townspeople consider her poor and needy? She quickly dismissed those thoughts, and moved into the kitchen where she continued to stir the stew, begun by Ragonde, and to prepare bread for dinner.

Behind her, Françoise and Anne were sitting on the floor playing with rag dolls. Loyse looked around on the table and saw a small leftover bit of bread dough and picked it up. She started to roll it into a ball.

"Maman?" Loyse cried out.

"Yes, Loyse?" replied Armande.

"Do we have to share a room with that strange girl?"

"For now, yes, you do," Armande replied.

"What's wrong with her arm?" inquired Anne. "It looks funny."

"It looks funny because she is crippled," replied Armande.

Loyse threw the dough ball at Anne and hit her in the back.

"Loyse!" yelled out Anne, who was now angry.

Loyse giggled and ran up the stairs.

"Loyse! Come back down here and apologize to your sister; I insist," Armande commanded.

"I'm sorry," Loyse sheepishly replied.

Armande, satisfied with her daughter's apology, returned to cooking.

"Is she really our sister?" Anne inquired as she turned in the direction of her mother.

Armande, quickly turning to face Anne, promptly replied, "Absolutely not."

Loyse interjected as if to point out her in-depth understanding of the entire matter, "Of course not. She's our stepsister. There's a difference, you know. "

Armande placed the bread in the warm brick oven in the yard, just outside the door, to help it rise; then, once back in the house, she looked in the direction of the big chest sitting on the floor in front of the stairs.

"Girls, come help me with the chest," instructed Armande. Armande and the two eldest girls walked toward the large chest. The two of them along with Armande pulled it into the center of the room, and there, Armande opened it. Inside were fine linens and tapestries of far greater quality and price than those already in the house. She had kept them from her previous marriage, and hoped, by taking them out of the chest, to use them as a reminder of the standards she ought to strive for in her new married life.

"This is our home now," Armande exclaimed as she thought aloud. "And we need to build a life that is prosperous and good."

Scurrying down the street, trying to keep at her father's side, Germaine's teary eyes were cast down to the ground.

"Keep your chin up. You're likely to run into something," her father said.

Suddenly, Germaine caught sight of Bernard, a forty-year-old homeless vagabond who regularly sat, begging, on the same street corner. In his hands he held out his hat, hoping for a few *sous* from any passerby who would notice him. He smiled at Germaine and Laurent Cousin, but only Germaine locked her eyes on the beggar while she tugged on her father's arm, hoping he would stop. Laurent discouraged his daughter from acknowledging the beggar, but Germaine's heart was empathetic to the poor man's situation. Was it her father's malicious sideways glance at the man? Was it something in the beggar's face, his demeanor, the hesitancy to meet other's eyes, the downward glance, so common by the rejected, that caught hold of her heart? These things are often hidden from inquiring eyes and minds, as they remain part of a mysterious realm, hidden from the intellect and from those anxious of life's tumultuous movements, but reserved for those quiet souls who fear not the suffering hardships of life. Germaine was such a pliable twig, so vulnerable, so weak, yet so resolute in answering love's never-ending call to selflessness and surrender. Turning to her papa she said, "Papa, this poor man suffers. Look at him on the ground."

Bernard was poor and alone, with nothing to eat, yet Laurent's heart remained cold, untouched by the man's plight. "*Non*, Germaine," Laurent replied, "we must get home promptly to help our new family settle in properly."

Germaine, overcome by sorrow, drew near to the pauper, his soul's misery affecting her profoundly. "But, papa," Germaine humbly replied, "he suffers, he suffers greatly."

"I said *non*, Germaine, we must go, it is late," Laurent insisted. "Leave this wretched creature, this scalawag of an unfortunate man. He made his choices."

Looking up at the father and daughter as they walked away, Laurent seemingly pulling Germaine by the hand, Bernard replied to the father's scornful reproach, "Bonjour and merci, monsieur!"

As Germaine turned one last time to get a final glimpse of him before getting into the carriage, Bernard looked once more in the direction of the young girl who had so beautifully wept for him.

"O thank you, mademoiselle, for your most precious tears!" Bernard murmured imperceptibly. He paused and watched them ride off.

As Laurent and Germaine rode back to the farm together, Germaine remained very quiet, tears streaming down her cheeks.

"Papa? Why did Madame Belchères have to leave?" Germaine asked.

"I know you're sad to see her go, but you'll see how things are going to turn around for us now. Come now, you knew her stay would be short. I got married quickly to make sure you had a new maman, so that she can take care of you."

Germaine did not respond. Laurent whipped the horses to go faster.

"Is there something that you need, Germaine?" Laurent asked.

"Can I help you in the field?" Germaine inquired.

Laurent frowned as he wiped sweat from his brow.

"I'm afraid you're still too small to help on the land, and your limp hand and arm do not help matters. But do you know what you could do to help?" proposed Laurent, looking to engage her and distract her.

"What, papa?" Germaine jumped excitedly.

"When we get back, you can help your new maman and new stepsisters get settled in. Make her and her children feel welcomed."

"I'd rather work in the field with you," Germaine replied. Laurent continued to look ahead as he directed the horses, purposely choosing not to respond until they reached the farm.

Once the carriage came to a halt in front of the farmhouse, Laurent turned to Germaine and said, "Come here, Germaine." Germaine moved over and sat next to Laurent, whose face showed some impatience. He reasoned with her: "I know this is an adjustment. But it's important we all learn to get along together. We're going to be a family now. And that has to start with you being brave enough to get to know them and helping them become familiar with their new home."

Laurent looked at her, got out of the carriage, and went to the other side to pick her up and place her on the ground. He got back into the carriage and began to drive off, but then suddenly halted the horses from about ten feet away. Turning around, he yelled: "Do you understand me, Germaine?"

"Oui, papa," replied Germaine.

"That's a good girl," Laurent replied. "Now run along while I go and do some plowing. I'll be home in two hours for supper."

Germaine began to walk in the direction of the farm house, her face a little uneasy. As she looked at the door, she put on a courageous expression before walking into the house.

Loyse, Anne, and Françoise were sitting around playing dolls while Armande continued making supper. Armande turned immediately in the direction of Germaine the moment she walked in.

"Well, that certainly took long enough. I suppose your father has gone to the field? Well, in any event, I need you to get water for dinner."

"O! Oui, madame; I'll get some water right away!" replied Germaine with the most joyful expression. She was determined to be as helpful as she could.

Germaine enthusiastically ran out the door, grabbing one pail with her able hand and hooking the second pail with her lame arm. She ran to the well and began to fill the first pail with water. Meanwhile, Loyse inspired the two others to concoct a plan to cause Germaine to spill the water. They snuck out of the house and followed Germaine from a distance, careful not to be seen. As Germaine struggled to carry the two buckets of water back to the house, the three girls, hidden behind trees, pulled a rope across Germaine's path just as she was walking by, catching her ankles and causing her to stumble forward, dropping the pails as she tumbled to the ground. The girls came out from hiding and began laughing at her. Completely drenched in water, she tried to laugh with her new sisters.

"Look, girls, the little monster is laughing at herself; she's too stupid to know any better," Loyse boisterously cried out.

"I must go and fetch more water for dinner," Germaine exclaimed, not quite understanding the disingenuous nature of her new stepsisters' intent.

She struggled to get to her feet, and then ran off in the direction of the well, soaked to the bone, with the two empty pails in hand.

"I don't know about you, but I think we should take credit for getting the water. Maman will then give us treats for being good and helpful," cried out Loyse to the two others.

The three girls waited for Germaine to fill her pails, and then followed her, from a distance, back to the house. When Germaine got to be about ten feet from the house, they rushed behind her and grabbed the pails from her hand and arm, entering the home with laughter. They yelled out, in unison, to their mother, "Maman! We all got the water together."

"Germaine dropped the water all over the ground. So Anne and Françoise helped me carry new pails of water back to the house. See what good girls we are," exclaimed Loyse, now satisfied that her cunning won her and her sisters approval points with their maman.

"Germaine, come here! Did I not explicitly ask you to get the water for dinner?" inquired Armande.

"O madame! But I did as you asked, but I accidently fell and…"

"You are completely soaked in water; a complete mess!" interjected Armande. "You fell? What kind of an excuse is that? If you fall, then you get back up and complete your task. That's the way things get done," Armande explained with impatience and pride.

Armande grabbed Germaine by the arm, pulled her close to her face, and said with a controlled voice, anger seeping from every syllable, "Have I made myself clear? In the future, you will do as I tell you."

Armande pushed Germaine away, ruffling her headscarf, and causing it to fall to her shoulders. Suddenly, the purplish abscesses on Germaine's neck were exposed—the scarf no longer completely covering them—horrifying Armande into shock.

"Oh my God! What are those sores on your neck?" exclaimed Armande, terrified and sickened by what she saw.

"I was born with these sores, madame. Maman use to care for them. Sometimes they go away for a time."

"I am most certainly not getting close to care for any of those sores. They are disgusting. I will simply not have it. Why, they could be dangerous to my children. What if they catch it? You despicable little runt, you stay away from my children," Armande cried, grabbing her children and holding them tightly, as if to shield them from a rabid dog.

"O! madame, I will be careful not to play around your children. I promise," said Germaine with genuine intent.

"You promise! My word, promises are not enough, Germaine, and so your intentions are meaningless. No, rather it is I who will be careful. I will speak to your father about this; for now, get out of the house; get out now, I tell you," Armande screamed.

That evening, while Armande and Laurent were getting ready to retire, Armande cautiously approached the topic of Germaine's sores. "Laurent, what are those abscesses on Germaine's neck? I knew nothing about them; you never informed me that your daughter was sick in this way. I saw them for the first time today and nearly fainted."

Laurent, feeling his new wife distraught, replied, "Well, I didn't think it important, Armande. The child functions like any other except for her lame right arm and hand, and so I just…"

Armande quickly rebutted, "Laurent, this is no trivial matter; your daughter is sick. Those purplish abscesses are large and they are disgusting to look at. They are from some kind of a revolting curse, and I will not have her close to my daughters; I will simply not allow it. You know, Laurent! These pustules are referred to as the king's evil. My God, they could catch whatever she has and also become ill."

"Armande, calm down," Laurent interjected, hoping to bring some reason to the discussion. "The child has had this from an early age. I don't think they are dangerous. I mean, we would have seen their nefarious effect already if there was one; I would have caught it, and other children she has encountered also would have been sickened," Laurent replied with a sense of urgency to counter and quell his new wife's fears as quickly as he could.

"Laurent, you are now responsible for three new children and a wife, and you must show some resolve at protecting us. This is not only your morale duty but, as the father of this family, it is your obligation," Armande replied.

"What can I do, Armande? I never thought this child to be a menace," Laurent reasoned.

"Oh! But she is Laurent, and I don't think it right at all to keep her around the house all day. The other children could be likewise cursed. These are my children, and I must protect them," Armande insisted.

"But what would you have me do, Armande?" inquired Laurent.

"From now on, I think she should watch the sheep, instead of the shepherd you now employ…what is his name?"

"It is Monsieur Laudin; he has been working for me for several years," replied Laurent, now fearful that his wife was cornering him to let go of his trusted worker.

"Well, in any event, I don't want her around the house or the other children," insisted Armande. "Being a shepherdess is a perfect way to keep her far from the children. I think that if we have Germaine, rather than Monsieur Laudin, shepherd the sheep, she would be far enough away from my children for most of the day. Think also of the money we could save. On the bright side, this would occupy her and give her a sense of purpose. I think it clear that her lame right hand and arm will not help you in the fields or me in the management of the household. This would benefit everyone. I will take her to the pasture myself tomorrow," she added, as if the matter had been settled. "We should also be thinking about alternative sleeping quarters for the child. What good would it be for her to be gone all day, only to be huddled in close quarters with my children at night while they sleep?"

Laurent, feeling that he was losing this battle, made one last attempt at reducing Germaine's plight: "But what sleeping quarters shall we give her? Perhaps by the fireplace downstairs?

"Laurent," Armande replied with insistence, "the child must be completely out of the house…in the barn perhaps."

"But the winters are frightfully cold, and the summers are hot; it would be terrible for her to be exposed to these kinds of harsh environments all day and night."

Armande moved behind Laurent to rub his shoulders as he sat in the chair removing his boots. "Non, Laurent, the cold in winter would help control the infection, plus there are warm blankets she could use. You know well that the sheep are known to keep the shepherds warm in cold weather since they tend to huddle together. I know this to be true, Laurent."

Laurent finally admitted, "Well, if you think it will make a difference, Germaine can go to the Manaut pasture to watch the sheep. I will break the news to Monsieur Laudin in the morning, but I will not agree to her living in the barn; the conditions would be unbearable for the child."

It did not take much for the matriarchal Armande to convince Laurent of the financial savings they would make by firing Monsieur Laudin and replacing him with the little Germaine. Sending Germaine to the barn would be a battle for another day.

That night in the children's bedroom, Loyse and Anne were sharing the bed that was once Germaine's, and Françoise was lying on the second bed. Germaine, kneeling in prayer on the floor, stared at her new bed, a wool mat, given to her by Armande. She silently offered the loss of her bed as a suffering she lifted up to heaven. She closed her eyes tightly and, clasping her hands together, she began to pray:

"Dear God, please look after papa in all his hard work, and, my Jesus, hear my prayer for a plentiful crop for this season. Also, my God, thank you for giving papa a new wife and a new family, and please watch over us. I pray to you, O Jesus, so that I can be a good daughter and sister. My God, please take care of maman for me in heaven and let her know how much I miss her. Amen."

Germaine, paying no mind to the snickering coming from the other children, lay down on the floor and covered herself with a blanket. She lay there, her eyes filled with tears as she listened to Loyse, Anne, and Françoise whispering.

"Her maman is in heaven?" asked Françoise.

"She's dead," replied Loyse.

"Well, that doesn't mean she's in heaven and that is for sure!" clarified Françoise, pridefully flaunting her knowledge of church matters.

"She could be burning in hell," added Anne. The three children giggled more. Germaine closed her eyes and covered her head with the blanket in an attempt to shield herself from the comments that had already wounded her to the very depth of her soul.

The next morning, Armande confronted Germaine. "I spoke with your father, and we think it best that you begin watching the sheep."

"Madame, I know nothing about being a shepherd," replied Germaine, concerned about her new assignment.

"You will learn! Today, you will take the sheep to the nearest pasture; do you know where that is?" inquired Armande.

"I do not, madame," exclaimed Germaine, now frightened by the task being assigned to her.

"It is up the main road at the Manaut pasture, where Monsieur Laudin has been bringing them. You will take them there and watch over them from sunrise until sundown. Don't waste your time, Germaine, while you are in the field! I expect you to complete your house chores when you get back. Do not disappoint me," warned Armande.

"I won't, madame," Germaine responded with a strong sense of anxiety building up inside.

"You will leave immediately," ordered Armande. "I will take you to the pasture myself."

"Oui, Madame," Germaine promptly responded.

"Good! Then I suggest you start gathering the sheep," the new matriarch commanded.

Armande led Germaine and the sheep to Manaut pasture, after ensuring that Laurent did dismiss Claude Laudin as promised. Once they were near the pasture, Armande acquainted Germaine with the many tasks that a shepherdess must do. Convinced that she had given the child sufficient instruction, Armande proceeded to pull out some scraps of bread from her apron, saying, "This is all you get, so don't be a glutton." Germaine took the bread and nodded. Then Armande left the child there, alone on the edge of the pasture. Germaine, carrying her staff, led the sheep into the valley. In no time, the herd surrounded the young shepherdess who walked in their midst, and eventually sprawled over the hillside.

After twenty minutes, Germaine sat on a rock to rest, and looked out over the sheep. She smiled as she contemplated the peacefulness of the pasture.

One and half months later, near the end of a late summer day, Laurent, while plowing the fields, saw Germaine a short distance away from him with the sheep around her. As she walked in his direction, Laurent stopped the horses.

"Germaine, were you a hardworking shepherdess today?"

"Oui, papa, in the Manaut pasture! See how all my sheep follow me," Germaine joyfully exclaimed.

"Is this work pleasing to you?" Laurent inquired.

"O yes, papa! The sheep are my new friends," she eagerly replied. "I have given them each a name."

"Go to the house now and get cleaned up," Laurent directed.

Germaine slowly walked in the direction of house, the sheep following behind her. As she approached, Ann and Loyse, giggling from games they were playing in the barn, saw Germaine walking towards them. They stood, waiting for her to approach, and then quickly hid behind the barn. As she got closer to the house, a rock hit Germaine in the forehead. Germaine touched her wounded head with her left hand, and as she drew her hand away, blood stained her palm and fingers. Germaine's eyes welled up as she noticed the two sisters laughing at her; she whimpered and ran in the direction of the house. The two sisters ran after her.

In the house, meanwhile, Armande was preparing dinner. Germaine ran into the house and looked at Armande.

"What are you carrying on about?" Armande sharply asked. Loyse and Ann quickly entered into the house.

"Nothing, madame, I tripped and fell," replied Germaine, visibly refraining from crying. Armande looked at Germaine's forehead and then at Anne and Loyse, who had practiced faces of innocence.

Armande turned to look at Germaine. "Well, don't be so awkward and watch where you are going next time. Now go clean yourself up, before you get blood everywhere." As she was turning her head away to resume cooking, she got a glimpse at the purplish abscesses protruding from Germaine's neck.

Armande grimaced in disgust as she realized the sores were draining down Germaine's neck. She stared at the sores for a moment, and then said: "Those sores on your neck…how long have they been leaking?"

"For about two weeks. I know they are ugly, but I am quite good about keeping them covered and clean," assured Germaine, with a voice straining to convey trust and confidence. Armande kept staring at the abomination that stood before her.

"I wash them every day, to help them get better," continued Germaine.

"I can't believe that your father kept this from me. Leaking sores?" She paused. "I suppose that I can put up with neck sores, but leaking sores can be very contagious," Armande cautioned. Germaine's embarrassment overwhelmed her to such a degree that she quickly covered her sores with her hand while pulling her scarf over her head, her tender eyes clearly distressed.

Armande, alarmed by what she saw, began yelling, "You ugly, pathetic creature! Surely you have done something to bring this curse upon yourself. Well, I will not let it in this house. Why, you are a threat to everyone in this household. Get out! Get out! You despicable, hideous monster! You will no longer live in this house. I will not have it…I will not allow you to bring the devil into this home. I must protect my children. I want you in the barn." Germaine froze in shock, as Armande's strident voice shattered the quiet of the afternoon.

"Get to the barn! Do you hear me?" Armande continued to shout. Germaine began moving slowly to the door. However, Armande, dissatisfied with Germaine's pace, grabbed her violently by the arm and shoved her out the door and through the yard.

"Out, I said! Get out this instant!" insisted Armande. The abusive stepmother pulled Germaine through the yard and pushed her out the gate. "Move, I tell you!" Armande continued insisting, as she pushed her in the direction of the barn. Once at the opening of the barn, Armande forcefully shoved Germaine to the ground.

"This is where you will stay," Armande barked. "This pit is the perfect place for you. You are a vile creature, Germaine. How it is that the Lord lets you live, I cannot comprehend. One thing is certain, and that is you will not live with us. Your curse will not come upon us." Armande, having pronounced her judgment, exited in a fury. Germaine now on her knees, began to sob.

Armande returned to the kitchen and resumed dinner preparations, her gestures and words clearly infected by reprimanding Germaine.

Suddenly, Loyse spoke up: "Do you need any help, maman?" She was trying to get on her mother's good side, sensing the tempest underneath Armande's cool demeanor waiting to explode.

At the dinner table that night, Laurent and Armande sat at opposite ends of the table. On one side were Françoise and Loyse, and Anne was on the other. Germaine's absence was noticeable, but none of the children dared to comment. Germaine was outside the house door, uncertain of whether to enter. She was hungry and cold from the night air.

Meat, potatoes, and vegetables were on the table. It was a good meal for a family of their size. Armande stood and served food on the plates of Françoise, Anne, Loyse, Laurent, and, finally, herself.

"Where is Germaine?" Laurent casually asked.

Armande, thinking about how to tell Laurent about Germaine's plight, looked in the direction of Loyse. "Would you please go and get her? She is likely still outside."

Loyse quickly got up from the table and ran to the door. As she opened it, she saw Germaine on the other side, cold, hungry, and frightened.

"Come in and eat," Loyse quickly said. Germaine entered, and then sat at the table next to Anne. All the plates were filled with food except hers. Armande looked at Germaine, her eyes severe and accusatory, and said with a condescending and impatient tone, "Those who do nothing to help out cannot be expected to be served in this family."

Everyone immediately began eating except Germaine; it was now clear that nobody was going to serve her. She stood and reached over to grab the wooden spoon so that she may fill her plate with a portion of food. Suddenly, Armande reached across the table and seized Germaine's hand as she was about to grasp the spoon. "This will be your last meal in the house, so be sure to enjoy it, Germaine," Armande forewarned.

Sitting back down, Germaine noticed that nobody had said grace before eating. She remained still, looking at her papa, who was voraciously slurping his food, expecting him to notice what he had forgotten to do. But no clarity of mind, no introspection, affected this man who was absorbed with filling his belly.

Experiencing some distress, she spoke up in haste, "But, papa, you haven't said grace."

"Oh, yes, of course," Laurent awkwardly responded, grunting and sighing in exasperation that his daughter found him at fault. "Grace…Yes, of course." Laurent instructed his wife and stepchildren to stop eating. Clearing his throat he quickly blessed himself and said, "Bless us, O Lord, and these thy gifts which we are about to receive from thy bounty, through Christ, our Lord. Amen."

Only Germaine's head was bowed and her eyes closed during the prayer. The others were impatiently waiting, their eyes wide open, anxious to get back to their food.

Turning to Armande, Laurent, attempting to detract from his embarrassment, said, "What do you mean by, this is to be Germaine's last meal in the house? I thought that we would be sharing meals together," Laurent continued, a sense of unease in his voice.

Armande responded, pretending not to have observed Laurent's awkwardness, "Not exactly; those abscesses on Germaine's neck are leaking all over her neck; neither bedroom nor food will my three children share with that child. Those leaking abscesses look dangerously contagious, and I will not put up with the foul smell that comes from them. Sharing a bedroom or meals with my children is out of the question, I am afraid, since all my children could get sick. We must keep the air clean. It might be advantageous if she sleep in another location."

"But where?" inquired Laurent.

"You know, Laurent, we discussed it previously. I was thinking the barn would be a perfect place to contain the infections."

"But it is much too cold in winter and hot in summer," replied Laurent.

"Not at all," retorted Armande. "The cold weather will help control the infection, and besides, there are some very thick covers she could use to keep herself warm in the winter. It is just too risky to keep her in the house. I've told you all of this already, Laurent. This must be Germaine's last meal, Laurent, if we are going to keep the air in the house clean. It is important that we be thorough in containing this curse if we want to protect my children. Don't you agree, Laurent?"

"Well, I just feel uneasy about this, but if you think it best for controlling her disease I suppose we should do it," Laurent responded with a disquiet sigh. As he turned to Germaine to confirm the situation, he suddenly noticed the cut on Germaine's forehead. "Germaine, what happened to your forehead? You have a horrible gash."

Again, reluctantly looking in the direction of her father, and then at Loyse and Anne, she said, "Nothing, Papa! I accidently hit my head."

"Well, you must be more careful," Laurent wisely counseled.

"*Oui*, papa. I will try." Germaine bowed her head in such a way that her sadness was not seen by her father.

Much later, in the middle of the winter months, Armande entered Jean Facet's residence and removed all of her winter garb. Louise Facet awaited Armande's arrival as she sat at the family dinner table with soup heating on the wood stove. As Armande entered the home, she complained, "It is cold enough to freeze a man to death out there!"

"No signs of letting up either," replied Louise Facet. "How is life treating you, Armande?"

"I'm surviving, my dear Louise, and nothing more!" replied Armande.

"Well, you may be better off than I am, then. I don't feel like I'm quite surviving," conceded Louise.

"Where have you been these last months?" asked Armande. "I have been mostly sleeping! That's all I seem capable of doing. I am so thankful for your help," Louise acknowledged.

"Well, the ladies of Pibrac are trying to rotate who does what for the sick and downtrodden of the parish. I am so sorry you are experiencing this poor health," Armande admitted.

"Yes, well, that is so kind of you, and all the ladies to help me and my family while I struggle with this illness. There is so much to do…and I just have no strength. Oh Armande! How do you even manage to put some time aside to come to my assistance in such a generous way?" Louise inquired with genuine interest. She held up her mug and sipped from it. "With all the troubles you have with that little Germaine! I just don't see how you can do it," Louise admitted.

"It is nothing, Louise, that any good Christian woman wouldn't be called to do. A little sacrifice here and there is very pleasing to our Lord, don't you know?" Armande answered.

Louise, showing interest in Armande's situation, inquired: "Tell me, my poor Armande! How are you managing with all three of your children in addition to that runt? The winters have been so cold, that I have also been wondering if you are warm enough…and have enough food? I worry about you and your children."

Armande complained bitterly: "The house is completely inadequate when it is so cold like this. It's as if the wind blows right through it. To make matters worse, the wood stove is not giving off enough heat, and the space is just not adequate. Ah! Louise."

"I know it is difficult, Armande, but the Lord is obviously giving you courage to endure these troubled times, especially with Françoise's influenza and Germaine's difficult behavior," Louise replied.

Now sniffling and crying, Armande continued, "We have so little room that I am concerned by the children's proximity to Germaine's open sores. I have kept her in the barn in hope of preventing those leaking, disgusting sores from infecting the other children. Oh my Lord! How I grieve having to put her in the barn to sleep, but what can I do? I have to admit that it's been a bit of relief for Laurent and I to get Germaine out of the house; it's so difficult to experience her disparaging behavior…. Ah! Laurent and I no longer know what to do. I mean, at night her rages used to disrupt the rest of the children; she is something else, I assure you. Her pious ways are a complete cover-up; she is devious and conspiring like the best of them. Don't be deceived by her religious practices," cautioned Armande.

"But hasn't Germaine's behavior improved in the last while? Did you not tell me she was more agreeable and gentle?" Louise asked.

Armande became visibly upset. She paused, closed her eyes, and said, "Laurent and I truly saw an improvement in her wicked behavior, and we took solace that only bright days lay ahead. But then I caught her again, negligent of her duties and stealing bread from the household. I swear that I have become tired of punishing her, and yet it is only the rod that can correct such a disruptive child. Stealing is simply not acceptable, but when she lies on top of always slacking on her duties, I have to do something! Why, just think of the scandal she creates for Anne, Françoise, and Loyse, who witness her behavior. I worry about the state of her soul."

"Oh my…Armande!" exclaimed Louise Facet. "I had no idea that you were going through so much! She just looks like such a harmless thing; who would have known?" Louise pondered for a second the likelihood of such an innocent and pious child being so deceitful. She continued, "How can you prevent such bad behavior from influencing your own children, infecting them with this type of deceit?"

"I solved that pretty quickly," Armande pridefully replied with an air of noble rectitude. "She now has the duty of shepherdess. I send her to tend to the sheep in the Manaut pasture near Chemin des Bourdettes; that is where Monsieur

Claude Laudin used to take the sheep when he worked for Laurent. Laurent and I believe this will finally help contain her mischievous behavior."

"I pray that it will…my poor Armande!" Louise replied with deep sympathy steeped in Christian charity. "How unsettling this all must be for your family," Louise pondered aloud.

It took some getting used to, but Germaine began to routinely bring the sheep to pasture on her own. One morning, she encountered a beggar lying by a tree while leading the sheep.

"Bonjour, monsieur," Germaine joyfully saluted the man.

He lifted his head, covered by a hood, his eyes darkened in part by the shadow it cast and by his threatening countenance.

"Bonjour," the beggar replied with a barely perceptible voice, his face worn by life's demanding trials, weathered by its fierce tempests.

As she approached him, she could see his face more clearly. It was the beggar she and her father had encountered a few weeks ago in Pibrac. Grief and shame suddenly came upon her as she remembered how cold her father had been towards him.

"Monsieur, what is your name again? I forgot it already," she asked, hoping to make amends for her father's offence and engage the man she felt was so abandoned. "My name is Germaine," she offered, to entice him to respond.

His sullen eyes, peering out from under the hood, remained unmoved by the little girl's inquiry. His silence was deafening.

She knelt down in front of him and, taking bread from her apron, she attempted to give him some of her mid day meal ration.

"Here, monsieur, you must be hungry. Please take the bread. I am so sorry for not having given you something when I was with my father the other day. I apologize for him; he was bothered with so many things."She bowed her head down low and added, "I am so sorry, monsieur, please forgive me."

Bernard, touched by the young girl's humility, decided to reply. "My name is Bernard, mademoiselle; you are forgiven."

He dusted off his tattered jacket and,pulling back his hood, said, "I saw you in tears several weeks ago…and today what do I see?But a beautiful smile…and no more tears, "Bernard pointedly observed. Touched by the child's simplicity and purity of heart, he reached into his pockets and pulled out a handful of bonbons,which he immediately handed over to the little shepherdess; a passerby had dropped them in his hat just a half-hour before. Germaine graciously took the pieces of candy, but then thought that her stepmother would be upset, so she offered to return them back to Bernard. He immediately refused to take them, exclaiming,"They are for you, mademoiselle!" Bernard winked at her. Germaine's smile widened as she put a piece of candy in her mouth. "Why were you crying several weeks ago? Dare I ask?"Bernard inquired. "I had to say good-bye to somebody," replied Germaine.

"Well, you know what the best thing about saying good-bye is?" Bernard happily suggested.

"What?" Germaine replied, dumfounded by the question.

"It always leads to a new hello," Bernard happily pointed out.

"Well, Monsieur Bernard, I have to bring the sheep to pasture, and so I must go quickly," Germaine exclaimed with insistence and a defined sense of urgency.

"That's too bad. Are you not a little young to be a shepherdess?" Bernard inquired.

"O! Non, monsieur. I am five years old and almost six. Thank you for the candy. I must go now," she responded, her brow gently frowning with determination and a strong sense of duty.

"O Germaine, it seems to me that your purpose is clear," Bernard acknowledged.

On Sunday morning the Cousin family sat in a pew near the front of the church. Father Jean gave the sermon, instructing the flock about the virtue of trust in God. He began, "Dear brothers and sisters in Christ, God in His mercy loves us unconditionally. Therefore, it seems to me that we ought to completely submit to God's design, and thus, practice a certain self-forgetfulness, self-effacement, and selflessness for it is good for the soul to strive to be wholly preoccupied with loving and obeying Him: the Alpha and the Omega, the Son of God.

Taking our gaze off the king of kings, invariably leads to the danger that we may become self-absorbed, concerned, shall we say, about these fears that needlessly affect us by swaying us from the path the Lord has drawn out for us. Let us instead strive to rid ourselves of all these fears and disquietudes, which cause us to fester in anxieties and worries. In the end, my dear children, these concerns that we hold on to are nothing but the consequences of self-love; it is rather the love of God that should preoccupy us. Does not the Virgin Mary represent for us an ideal model of surrender to God's will? To follow Mary's example is to be always content with God even if the worse things may happen to us or if we become troubled interiorly. You must bend like a reed in the wind, never resisting the gales, but conforming to them. My dear souls, don't you know that it is the strong and unyielding tree that is pulled from its roots and breaks under the force of the great tempests? We mustn't oppose God's will, but conform to it with all of our heart. Simply trust that His infinite wisdom will guide you, purifying you a little so that you may earn the merits needed for eternal life. Be watchful then, that the path you follow be straight and narrow, allowing little to no distractions that may overwhelm you with undisciplined and imprudent reflections that lead to your own peril. Be mindful of keeping your intentions pure and good, and fight the temptation of entering those deep cavernous thoughts and worries that can lead to troubles, to interior concerns rooted in love of self. The Lord will give you the graces to assist you…He will not abandon you. We are our own greatest enemy my children, so entrust your lives to our Lord Jesus Christ, and run from the illusions that we are self-reliant and strong. That, my children, I tell you in truth, we are not. Believe me when I say that believing in your own strength is the beginning of what could be considered as your demise. The parishioners were stirring in their pews by the time the priest finished his homily, for nobody seemed to understand the profundity of his reflection, except for the most salient points: God loves us endlessly and that we should not love ourselves too much. Germaine, on the other hand, was touched to the very core of her soul, despite being six years old, for her mind locked on to the image of the reed bending in the wind. She could see herself as a reed, and now understood a little more clearly that her life as a shepherdess living in a barn is nothing but God's will for her, and that she ought not complain or resist. Germaine found the idea of always being content with God to be most pleasing for who else could she trust, but Jesus, since her whole family had turned from her, leaving her alone and abandoned. But now joy filled her heart with the notion that Jesus was near; she was not alone. Finally, it was time for communion; Fathers Jean and Guillaume were giving communion at the front of the church. The faithful were kneeling around the altar rail, waiting to receive communion on their tongues. Germaine and Françoise were the only ones left in the pew where the Cousin family was sitting. Germaine looked at the people receiving communion with great envy, wishing one day that she too could partake in the Lord's supper, while Françoise, twiddling her thumbs and kicking her legs back and forth, thought about ways she could play pranks on Germaine.

When mass had ended, Laurent gestured to Armande that he would like to introduce her to Fathers Sabrières and Carrière. They genuflected in front of the sanctuary and proceeded, with the children trailing behind, to enter the sacristy where the priests were removing their vestments.

"I'd like to formally introduce you to my new wife, Armande," said Laurent to Father Sabrières. Armande extended her hand, which Father Jean gently held in both his hands.

"So very nice to meet you, Madame Cousin," Father Sabrières greeted.

Father Jean released Armande's hand, and quickly Father Guillaume in turn clasped it in both of his, saying, "Welcome to the parish, madame."

Father Jean looked intently at Germaine, and said, "And how are you this fine day, Germaine?"

"Fine, thank you, Father," she replied, surprised that the priest would even address her.

"I noticed that you are not attending catechism on Sunday afternoon. This would be a good thing for you, Germaine. It is necessary if you desire to take communion when you are older. Would you like that?" Father Sabrières gently inquired.

"O! Yes, most certainly, Father," Germaine enthusiastically answered.

Looking at Germaine's parents, Father Sabrières explained, "It's about time for Germaine to begin catechism classes in the afternoons on Sundays with the rest of the parish children, don't you agree, Laurent?"

"Yes, well I think it would be good, but she also must take the sheep to pasture as well," Laurent replied timidly. He always felt intimidated by priests.

"Well then, that settles it," promptly concluded Father Sabrières. "You'll make sure she's at the church at two p.m. on Sundays?"

Armande, becoming a little unsettled by the priest's questions and intrusion into Germaine's education, quickly addressed a question to Father Guillaume in order to deflect attention away from Germaine.

"Father, to whom would I speak if I had some weaving I would like to donate to the parish?"

Father Jean opened his mouth to respond, but Father Guillaume beat him to it. "I would be so pleased to receive them from you, madame. How nice of you. When should we expect them?" asked Father Guillaume.

In the church, Madame Leguard's husband grabbed his wife by the arm and escorted her to the door. She was trying to hold her children's hands, but she kept fumbling with them as he moved her angrily out the door. Everyone could see the distress in Madame Leguard's face. Her husband had suspected, for quite some time, that she was having an affair with Jean Facet, but he could not prove it; the suspicion was fueling a temper he had at times difficulty containing.

The Cousin family walked down the street. Up ahead was Bernard, sitting with his back against a wall in the same place Germaine had first seen him with her father. Upon seeing him, Germaine rushed up to him.

Armande looked on as Germaine and Bernard exchange inaudible small talk. Germaine handed him something and then ran back to her family.

"What did you give that beggar?" Armande sternly asked.

"Just a piece of candy," replied Germaine sheepishly.

"And where would you get candy from?" Armande quickly inquired.

"Monsieur Bernard gave me some a week or so ago. I kept a piece to give back to him. He's very nice, you know."

"Stupid child," Armande shrieked. "How dare you accept candy from a dirty beggar, especially one like that? Did you share any with the other children?" Armande asked with a tone of accusation and malice. Armande looked to her children, who all shook their heads. Armande continued, "Germaine, we have a reputation to uphold. You are not to take anything from that man again, do you hear me?"

"I do, madame," Germaine softly responded, her eyes submissively looking downward.

The next day, Armande headed to Pibrac to acquire some provisions from the marketplace. As she walked through the town square holding a basket, Armande impatiently waited for a boy, herding a small flock of goats, to cross in front of her. Afterward, she then moved swiftly to the bean cart, parked amongst many other vendors displaying various goods.

"Armande! How are we today?" said the bean lady.

"I have been better, and I see the price of your beans will not improve my disposition," Armande stoically replied.

"Madame, our prices are what they must be, and for this I apologize," the bean lady retorted.

"Well, I don't suppose you have much control. I will take two bundles," Armande answered with some poise. The bean woman began to assemble two bundles of beans as Armande searched her apron pockets for the money to complete the purchase.

"How is your new stepdaughter?" inquired the bean lady as she was preparing the order.

"That little pious twit? I can't tell you what a trial she is to me," responded Armande insistently.

The bean lady rejoined, "She appears to be a bit of an idiot."

"O! That she is. The mongrel is clearly too stupid for school; the leaking infection from her neck is a threat to all the children. So, to get her away from the house and the children, I have been sending her to shepherd the sheep in the Manaut pasture. There, she is no bother to anyone," replied Armande.

The woman handed Armande her beans saying, "Here you are, Madame Cousin: two bundles."

Armande exchanged her money for the beans without a word, her demeanor serious. As she prepared to walk away, she turned to the merchant, and said, "Thank you, madame. Have a pleasant day."

Meanwhile, back at the Cousin farm, Pierre Dauvet, Laurent Cousin's farmhand, led an ox through the field, pulling a large crate half filled with parsnips.

Laurent was harvesting wheat in the adjacent field. As the farmhand drew nearer to the area where the two fields met, Laurent stopped his work and went to meet him. Laurent came around the back of the ox and looked into the crate and said with some alarm in his voice, "This is it?"

The worker replied, "I've been telling you, sir, that things haven't been growing right out here for some time now; it might be all that rain we've been getting." Laurent picked up a handful of parsnips from the crate and examined them. He then dropped them back into the cart and walked in the direction of the field from where the parsnips were being harvested. The farmhand dropped the reins of the ox and followed after him. The two of them stood over a completely unhealthy row of parsnips.

"I cannot believe this! Surely I am cursed," Laurent exclaimed with frustration straining his voice. "Why the Lord would do this to me, I do not know!" He sighed in defeat.

"What do you think it is, sir?" questioned the farmhand.

"It is my fault. I'm a fool for not rotating the crops. I was supposed to leave this field fallow this year and, money being what it is, I thought I might increase my harvest yield by cultivating here one more season. Now I've lost all the money I spent planting here, and I will have two fallow fields next year with no income at all!"

Laurent turned and left with both his hands on his head shaking in shame. The farmhand watched as Laurent headed back to the wheat field.

The next morning in the Cousin barn, Germaine, asleep on a bed of hay, was covered in sheepskins. The sun had just come up over the hill and gently bathed her face in an angelic splendor of light. Armande suddenly burst into the barn like a tempest about to lay waste homes and trees.

"Wake up, you lazy thing, and get up!" Armande commanded with overbearing authority. Germaine awakened and sat up instantly, leaving her scrofula neck sores fully exposed.

"Cover up that horrible curse," cried Armande. Germaine quickly found her scarf and wrapped it over her head and around her neck as she jumped to her feet.

"Sorry, madame. I'll begin gathering the sheep right away," replied Germaine, feverishly trying to cover herself.

"I spoke with your father yesterday about how you are hardly good for anything around here. You neglect to complete your farm duties after you get back with the sheep. And so I've decided that you will spin wool, five bundles a day when you are out with the sheep; this will correct your lazy demeanor," proclaimed Armande with decisiveness.

"Madame, I'm sorry about not completing my chores. I fell asleep...," explained Germaine. But no sooner had she blurted out her explanation than Armande struck Germaine across the face with a blow strong enough to cause her to fall backwards and onto the ground.

"Excuses, I don't want to hear excuses, I want work done, and done well!" yelled Armande, her voice screeching with anger. Germaine sat up in shock, her hands on her face, blood dripping from the nose

"I…I…," whispered Germaine, barely able to express her surprise.

"I don't want to hear anything come out of your mouth. You are now a shepherdess and a weaver. Those are things you will do from now on. And let the fear of Almighty God come upon you should you fail in these tasks, Germaine. I will see to it that you pay severely," Armande said sternly. The field's poor harvest had strained the family severely enough that Armande's anger about falling deeper into poverty could not be contained.

Without saying a word, Germaine took a staff and the wool, and nodded in acknowledgement of her newly assigned duties. She left for the field with the sheep following behind her.

The next day, the Cousin children, Loyse, Françoise, and Anne, rose early, excited about playing a mischievous trick they had concocted the night before on the poor and unsuspecting Germaine. They were determined to put pitch in Germaine's clothing, before her clothes were brought out to her. They carried out their malicious deeds, laughing as they spread the pitch. They also rushed to the kitchen and found her porridge, which their mother had just finished preparing that morning. Loyse said to Anne, "Here, Anne, take the lye and mix it with Germaine's bowl of porridge." She mixed the lye as directed. Loyse then turned to her other sister and said, "Françoise, did you thoroughly spread the pitch in Germaine's clothes?"

Anne replied, "She did, and I helped her! When Germaine puts on her tunic she'll go crazy with itching! Oh, it's going to be so funny!" Upon hearing of the children's plans, Armande nodded approvingly with a smirk drawn across her lips.

"Now settle down children! Stop making such a fuss," Armande cautioned.

Anne brought Germaine's clothes and porridge to the barn. Germaine took both graciously with a smile.

"Thank you, Anne! The porridge looks delicious. Oh, and the tunic and cloak look so clean. Thank you!"

This was the first set of clean rags she had received since being cast into the barn.

Anne left the barn slowly, hoping to hear Germaine's cry when she ate the porridge. Anne turned, pretending to walk away, but smiled in anticipation of the screams she expected to hear.

As Germaine placed the tunic over her head, she gasped in horror as the pitch spread all over her body and began to increasingly irritate her skin. She rolled around in the dirt trying to sooth the uncomfortable irritation. She finally settled, having not uttered a single sound, collecting herself prayerfully in order to offer this suffering to the Lord as Father Jean had taught in his many homilies. Then she bent down to pick up the bowl of porridge, which she anticipated would be delicious. After the first spoonful, in horror she spat right out of her mouth what she hadn't swallowed, as if it were pure fire. She fell to her knees as a strong burning sensation moved down her throat into her stomach. Sweat began streaming down her brow as the fire pit in her gut began to consume her from within with swelling strength. As if she was uttering her last words, she said, "My Lord, I surrender to you this fire for the conversion of my sisters. Take it, I beg of you." She quickly was drawn out of prayer as she retched up the rest of her gastric contents. Looking down at what she had vomited, she knew that without food she would go hungry and have difficulty completing the tasks demanded by Armande. The fear of being beaten prompted her to close her eyes and kneel on the ground, where she sought refuge in the arms of Jesus, the only one she could trust.

"O my Jesus," she whispered. "Help me not be too hungry today." Opening her eyes, she looked down at the porridge bowl she had dropped on the ground, picked it up, and began to eat from it. Anne, who had been peering through the cracks in the barn, was frozen in astonishment as she witnessed Germaine eating the porridge as if no lye had been added. The tunic she had been wearing did not seem to bother her either.

Realizing that the pitch and lye did not produce the desired effects, Anne, determined to see Germaine severely beaten, fabricated a story that the young shepherdess had called her terrible names.

That night, Armande entered the barn in a rage, accusing Germaine of poorly treating her Anne in addition to not meeting her wool-spinning quota for the day. Armande's rage clearly alarmed Germaine, as she saw her stepmother pick up the broom hanging by the barn door.

"Oh, non! Madame, not the broom," Germaine yelled out in terror.

"You did not do nearly enough weaving today. Look at all the wool that is left." Armande waved the leftover wool in her left hand. "What am I to do with you? And now I hear that you are insulting my children with vile names. You are a miserable, wretched child, a vile thing. I will teach you not to speak of others like that," Armande threatened with a raging voice.

Armande began to beat Germaine with the broom, and then, turning the broom around, she proceeded to strike the little thing with the handle over her body and head.

Germaine, hands over her head, yelled out, "I am so sorry, madame! I was so tired that I fell asleep weaving and did not finish."

Germaine fell into the corner of the barn and, crouching into a ball, tried to protect herself against the painful blows; however, Armande persisted to hit harder.

"But I never called your daughter any kind of name. I promise," Germaine yelled out, before a blow hit her on the side of the head, knocking her unconscious. Armande, standing over her motionless body, contemplated delivering further blows, but relented. Beatings of this kind went on frequently for years. Germaine expected them as she expected the day to follow night. The only comfort she got was from the little parts of the homilies at mass that she could understand. She learned about surrendering to Jesus's will, to trust in him. Father Jean-Granet Sabrières frequently described how many of Jesus's disciples had abandoned him at his passion. How that image saddened her terribly and helped her to grow with the resolution that she would not abandon Jesus, especially in his suffering. She understood something about the importance of consoling Jesus; this she could do. The thought of the many storms raging at the base of the mountain, described by Father Sabrières, with the cross at the sunny peak, was something she also frequently embraced and held on to for dear life. This she could understand somewhat, but oh! how difficult it was for her to climb that slope, for the tempests she had to face were indeed fierce.

6

When Death Comes Knocking

*"For you yourselves know perfectly, that the day of the
Lord shall socome, as a thief in the night."*

—1 Thessalonians 5:2 (Douay-Rheims Version)

The night had been unusually dark and calm, the October air unseasonably cold. It was 1586, and Germaine was now seven years old. The moon, partially hidden by an overcast sky, gently colored the fields in faded strokes of pale light. Anne, the middle child of Armande's three daughters, awoke calling for her maman; it was two in the morning. Feverish and chilled, she had thrown up all over the bed. Armande rushed into the children's bedroom, awakened by Anne's moaning; the two other children, undisturbed by the clamor, continued to sleep soundly. Alarmed by the child's fever and tremors, she awoke Laurent, ordering him to get the doctor. Off into the night rode Laurent, whip in hand, as he urgently pressed the horses on, shouting commands with a strong sense of urgency.

Several hours had passed, and Armande was still attempting to keep the child calm and comfortable, sponging her forehead with cold water, trying to appease the fever. *Laurent is taking too long to get back with the doctor,* she thought. *What could be keeping him?* Suddenly, more vomit came spewing out of Anne's mouth, but this time colored in blood. Armande's eyes opened wide with alarm, as she yelled to God in protest: "God, leave this child alone; why would you chastise this little one? She is but a child; leave her alone," Armande screamed to the benevolent God, the King of kings, the Lord of lords. As she was cleaning up the vomit, the door opened suddenly, and both the doctor and Laurent rushed in, the cool night air flowing into the house after them. This time, the ruckus awoke the two other children. Dr. Baillet moved quickly to the side of the bed and went right to work closely examining the child.

Lifting his head, after a few minutes of palpating Anne's chest, neck, and abdomen, and after closely inspecting the red sores on her arms, legs and chest, he frowned with concern and worry. The swelling of the child's neck glands, he had seen before, and the red buboes were also quite familiar. Wiping his brow with his handkerchief, he said, "My dear Laurent and Armande, Anne has what appears to be the plague." He paused and then clarified, "I am afraid to admit, it may be the bubonic plague. This pestilence's fiercest period was hundreds of years ago, but it now comes in waves, killing the young and the elderly. There is very little that I can do at this stage, but I believe that calling a priest would be very wise."

Armande was shocked and devastated, shouting out in distress and rage, "Non! Non! Non! It cannot be. My little Anne, my precious lamb, what am I to do?" It was purely a rhetorical question, one that demanded no reply, for in her heart she knew the answer.

Concerned by Armande's response, Dr. Baillet then added, "In the meantime, I can perhaps give her a lavage and do a little bloodletting in order to cleanse the infection and toxin from her system; perhaps this could help her. But foremost, you need to isolate the child as it is not clear how badly contaminated the surrounding air may be."

Laurent replied, "Anything you can do to save her, my good doctor, would be so appreciated by both Armande and I." Laurent got up and took the two other children downstairs.

Sitting in a chair close to Anne's bed, Armande's eyes had darkened, and her countenance was now miserable and austere, her spirit bound by hopelessness. And there, steeped in a misery for which she found no solace, no calm or peace, her anger rose, like the lava of a volcano now ready to flow with explosive force. In her soul she knew that Germaine was somehow responsible for this tragedy; the infection on her neck was surely the cause. She had perhaps not acted fast enough to get the child out of the house and away from her own children; she should have expelled her sooner. The grief she felt for not being diligent was unbearable. In the back of the room Dr. Baillet discussed with

Laurent how to keep Anne comfortable. Without removing all hope of recovery, Dr. Baillet urged Laurent to move in haste to get one of the priests. The doctor then bid Laurent and Armande good day, and promptly left, as he still had Madame Bonsecours to attend to before his daily consultations began.

Armande sat by her sick daughter's bedside, gazing out of the window, with eyes desolate and disheartened, forlorn that God had abandoned her; she was despondent and unreceptive to any consolations given to her by Laurent; her heart had now become cold with rage and hate.

After Laurent had returned with Father Guillaume for the extreme unction and viaticum, she proceeded to put her long coat over her shoulders and left the house. She walked directly to the barn, her eyes determined and her rage irrepressible; she had a clear purpose. It was 5:15 a.m.

Germaine was already awake, kneeling in the hay before the crucifix she had reverently placed on the small altar in the barn. The sheep were scattered around her, as if patiently waiting for Germaine to call their names before heading out to the pasture.

Like a full raging whirlwind, Armande entered the barn and grabbed the broom she had left behind after beating Germaine one August night a few months back. The sheep, sensing trouble, gathered more tightly around Germaine, as if to form a protective shield. Quickly, though, Armande confounded their plans, as she managed to scatter the sheep with a shriek, while waving the broom handle in circles around her, threatening the sheep if they did not move.

Suddenly, Armande was looking down at Germaine, the sheep now scattered to the side. Germaine was kneeling before the makeshift altar that was partially covered in hay and pigeon dung. A sight for sore eyes indeed, but not enough for Armande to mercifully relent from the beating she was about to administer. Germaine knew full well what was coming; she had experienced the beatings before with great frequency. This time, however, she sensed something different; Armande was not exhibiting her normal anger and impatience.

"Your neck infection has contaminated my children," Armande gravely said, as if she were about to pronounce the sentencing of a condemned prisoner. "Right now, Anne is fighting for her life, and it is all your doing. I should have protected her better from you; your leaking abscesses, disgusting as they are, will kill us all. She is vulnerable because she is so young; you infected her and will likely be the cause of her death. Damn you, Germaine! May hell swallow you up after I finish breaking every bone in your body."

No sooner did she finish her threat that Armande seized the broom with both hands and, after breaking the broom end by slamming it against one of the sturdy barn posts, ferociously struck Germaine across the head with the wooden end. Then again, she struck her face, knocking her out cold before she hit her head on a pail lying on the ground behind her. As Armande continued to strike Germaine on the torso, arms, and legs, she ordered her to get up, but Germaine remained motionless, blood streaming from her mouth and nose. Armande suddenly became agitated as she contemplated the consequences she would have

118

to face if she were accused and convicted of murdering her stepdaughter. She approached the child's body, and with the broom handle, attempted to stir her with it; but she remained unresponsive. Then she shouted, "Get up now, you worthless thing! I said get up!" Still Germaine did not move, blood now dripping out of her right ear. Armande concluded that one of the blows she leveled at her had to have been strong enough to kill her. Now terribly frightened, she knew that she had to dispose of her body before anyone found out. She had already concocted a lie about Germaine leaving early with the sheep. Perhaps they would believe she was eaten by wolves. Suddenly, she realized that since the sheep were all still in the barn, she would have to take them to the pasture and let them loose at the risk of many getting lost. She exited the barn quickly to locate a shovel to dig Germaine's grave.

Once Armande had left the barn, a stupendously beautiful angel suddenly appeared, emanating a light so bright, no human still in the temporal realm could look at it directly without going blind instantly. It was Germaine's guardian angel, who had crossed the veil under the specific command of God the Father. Approaching Germaine, he gently touched her head with his hand. It seemed as if a light had gone from the angelic entity and shimmered around, first her head and then her complete body, and finally disappeared into her chest as the angel faded away. Germaine's eyes opened suddenly, just as Armande entered the barn with a shovel.

"Ah! You are awake!" Armande voiced with surprise and a slight relief in her voice. "Get up now and take those sheep to pasture. Do not delay," she grumbled and finally returned to the house. Germaine wiped the blood from her nose and mouth, and began to call the sheep by name, gathering them around her like a good shepherd, and hiked in the direction of the field.

As Armande entered the home, the atmosphere had transitioned into darkness. Anne had passed into the next world; Laurent was listening as Father Guillaume recited the prayers for the dead. Armande's eyes were empty and lifeless. What more could she do? Exhausted, she went to her bed to lie down; Laurent saw the priest out; it was now 6:00 a.m.

As is the case when divine protection is lifted from souls that have become cold, angry, and steeped in mortal sin, tragedy strikes most severely because of the great love of the Father for those souls. Indeed, God, out of mercy and love for the soul, in allowing difficulties and tragedies, attempts to stir the individual into repentance. It sometimes seems that these trials the Lord sends us are more than what any mortal could endure. The case of Armande de Rajol, now Madame Cousin, brings great pause, for indeed, before long, Françoise would also be suddenly taken from this world.

7

From Sin Enters Darkness

"But he that hateth his brother, is in darkness, and walketh in darkness, and knoweth not whither he goeth; because the darkness hath blinded his eyes.

—1 John 2:11 (Douay-Rheims Version)

Inside the Facet household that evening, things were rather dark. Louise Facet sat in a rocking chair, staring at the door; hopelessness drew expressions of despair and sadness on her face. A moment later, Jean Facet came through the door, a startled look upon his face, as his wife sat there to greet him.

"Oh, hello dear," responded Jean. "Are the children up as well?" Facet asked with a practiced air of genuineness.

Seeing through the deception, Louise Facet retorted sharply, "Where have you been?"

"I told you, dear, that I was going fishing," replied Jean, now feeling the beginnings of an inquisition.

"That was six hours ago," Louise quickly replied. "It's dark. Where are the fish?" inquired Louise, who smelled a lie. Jean had been with Claire Leguard, and it was clear to Louise that her husband's countenance screamed out deceit; she had been noticing for some time that his mannerisms had become more mischievous, his conduct less virtuous.

"It took quite some time to get a decent price, but I finally sold them; now, I am tired and ready for food," Jean declared with authority.

"Let me see," rejoined Louise who at this point sensed fear in her husband.

"Let you see what?" replied Jean Facet, who was feeling cornered. "I told you I am tired and I am hungry. What is there left to eat from supper?" demanded Jean.

"Hand over the money you made from the fish," Louise somberly requested.

"I will not. And you watch your tone with me, woman. I have no need to answer to you. Now what is there to eat?" blasted Jean, who felt the details of his story derail. Louise Facet stared at her husband as he removed his boots.

"There is stew in the pot," Louise instructed dryly as she exited the room to go to bed. Facet angrily grabbed a wooden spoon and pulled the pot off the fire. He sat before the dying embers in the fireplace and ate what was left of the stew in pensive and somber silence. *Ah! how life has become burdensome!* he thought. It had already been two years since he had uncovered those inconsistencies in the deeds belonging to those Pibrac property owners. Had he not signed off on the deeds despite the misappropriation of funds, those investors from Lyon would not have gone through with the purchase of the land and buildings. It's only clear now that the sale of those properties benefited the community of Pibrac through important economic growth. He thought, *They were such unnoticeable modifications that, in the end, what did it matter? I almost didn't accept the bribe or sign off on the deeds. I was fearful that someone would catch the misrepresentations and the misappropriation of funds, but in the end, nobody did. The financial benefit to me was substantive, and the money that went to the "Bread for the Poor" campaign really paid off as well, as my reputation as an organizer and a benevolent community leader grew. The priests and bishop, in particular, thought highly of my skills as an organizer. Had I let fear govern me and prevent me from signing off on the deeds prior to meeting with the Panse family, no economic fallout would have been felt in Pibrac, and far less bread would have been distributed to the poor.*

In the end, no legal issues arose from those small and unnoticeable variances, his reputation only got enhanced, and his personal wealth increased over time. Pibrac's economy, contrary to what everyone had anticipated, did not suffer a collapse, and many opportunities he expected would come his way did in fact benefit him and his family indirectly.

Everything is well with my household; wealth, love, and a social standing like I have never experienced before have come like blessings, yet why am I tortured inside? The Lord must surely be pleased with what I have accomplished for the poor. What more does he want of me? he thought to himself.

He now recognized that the tension building between him and Louise was wearing him down. *Perhaps I should capitalize on my friendship with the pastor of St. Mary Magdalene Church and discuss whether he would recommend me to the position of city councilman,* he pondered. *Maybe this kind of involvement could take away this tension.* His ultimate goal was to get appointed to the Commerce and Development Committee so that he could oversee the economic expansion of the town. That kind of power would bring countless opportunities to grease his bank account with almost endless consulting work. He checked his meeting schedule and noticed that he did in fact have a scheduled appointment with Father Sabrières that coming Friday regarding the next year's Food for the Poor campaign. He would try then to get the pastor to recommend him for councilman.

"Well, it looks like it's settled, then," concluded Father Sabrières as he turned in the direction of Jean Facet.

"Indeed, I believe the goals of next year's campaign, while ambitious, can be achieved as long as the bishop supports the expansion," affirmed Jean.

"I shall write to him this afternoon," Father Sabrières said resolutely as he shuffled his papers into his case and placed it under his arm.

"Father, I wanted to ask you if you would be so kind as to mention my name to Monsieur le Maire, at the opportune time, of course, as a candidate for city councilman. I would greatly appreciate if you could," Jean said with concerted determination.

The pastor put his case back down on the table, and looked at Jean with serious and concerned eyes.

"Jean, you have become worldly; you seek advancement, social status, and wealth. What has become of you?"

"Father Sabrières, that's not true. Why, look at all the good I have done with the Bread for the Poor campaign. Surely there is nothing wrong with gaining some notoriety in the process," Jean swiftly retorted.

"There is more going on here than meets the eye, Jean. Let me ask you this: when was the last time you went to mass? How about confession?" inquired the priest.

"Father, God is with me; it is very clear…just look at all the graces I have received," Jean pointed out.

"Jean, don't kid yourself!" the pastor responded, like a father to a difficult son. "What are you thinking, Jean? That suddenly it's no longer necessary to examine your conscience and confess your sins?"

"I do examine my conscience and I do not find it necessary to confess anything to a priest," Jean shot back. He had wanted to tell off a priest like that for a long time.

"Don't believe for a minute that financial wealth is a sign of God's blessing. When the Lord truly approaches man, He weakens him, rather than strengthens. You are making the ghastly error of thinking that you are getting closer to God through the Bread for the Poor campaign, when in fact it is rather Him who approaches you. And when He does, Jean, He makes you spiritually, physically, and mentally weak."

"Father, why would God want to weaken me? That makes no sense to me," replied Jean with a conceited smile.

"Jean, it is this very weakness He desires so that there may be room for His might," the priest counseled.

"Jesus wants me weak? I have trouble believing that, Father," Jean defensively rejoined.

"All things are from God, and that includes any strength He gives. It is not yours to boast of, or to be proud of. This strength is the Lord's and only His. The danger, Jean, is that we claim that strength as our own; it is not. And, for love of the soul, it is for that reason that Jesus removes this self-assurance that we may feel, so that we can stop believing in our strength, our goodness, our abilities and wealth. He wants you to trust in Him, not yourself, Jean," Father Sabrières prayerfully observed.

Jean Facet stared at the pastor, unable to wrap his mind around what he was saying. It seemed simple enough, but he could not let it sink in. It was too foreign. He finally said, "I cannot accept this idea of weakness. I want to be strong, financially, and physically healthy. Are you implying that I am not living in God's graces because I am strong and wealthy?"

"Give glory to His name for all that He does for you, but be assured of this, that any sense of internal misery and corruption is a sign that Jesus is near but hidden and withdrawn, so that you may annihilate your self-love, the true barrier to God's grace." The priest paused, and then, as if inspired, concluded,

"I don't know the reason for this, Jean, but the sin of pride has taken hold of you. I've seen this before," the priest admitted, as he slammed his hands down on the table with such force that it shook Jean to the core. The pastor looked up at Jean, standing there white as a ghost, and said, "What serious sin are you involved in, Jean? Confess it this instant, for the love of God!"

Jean was dumbfounded that the priest had not only the audacity but also the clarity to infer that he was involved in serious sin. Jean knew that adultery had been ruling his life for quite some time. His mouth opened in astonishment, but still he refuted vehemently that serious sin was tainting his life in any way.

"I tell you, Father Sabrières, you are wrong, I swear it," protested Jean Facet.

"Do not swear to anything, Jean." He placed his case back under his arm and politely said as he was exiting, "In any event, if I can, I will put in a good word for you with Monsieur le Maire when I see him." He quickly left, closing the door behind him.

Inside the Cousin barn, Germaine, now nine years old, broken broom in hand, swept the floor with difficulty as the broom kept slipping from the grasp of her lame hand. Suddenly, Armande burst into the barn in a furious rage, just as Germaine had picked up the broom for the eighth time.

"You terrible child," Armande shouted stridently. "What have you been doing out here? I wanted you to feed the sheep and bring in the water. Is that too difficult to do? You have been playing out here, I suppose, like a spoiled, lazy child?" Armande yelled out the accusations, grabbing the broom from the child's hands.

"O non, madame," promptly countered Germaine in defense of her fruitless efforts. "I have done as you have told me, but I have trouble lifting the pitchfork; it is too big for me, and my right hand is too weak to get a good grasp of the broom. And the water bucket…"

"Enough!" shouted Armande. "I have never heard a child complain so much. You are nothing but an ungrateful creature deserving of a beating." Armande's red, flushed face betrayed her anger and hatred of the child.

Her hand held high, she struck the child's face and head until the little thing fell to the ground. Taking the broom handle with her other hand, Armande began to strike Germaine with the broom. The girl, now on her knees, shielded herself with her arms, covering her head from the onslaught of strikes. In her rage, Armande then began to use the broom handle to hit the girl on her arms, side, and legs. Germaine could not completely shield her body from the devastating blows of the handle. Now crouched into a ball, she screamed out, "I am so sorry, madame. I will finish my work, but please don't hit anymore." Armande continued striking her, this time in the face with the broom handle, and again on the head, giving no evidence that she intended to relent.

"*Sorry?* That is not good enough. You will learn, Germaine, to do your work. I will not tolerate laziness," Armande sternly warned, her rage increasing, so it seemed, with every strike.

Feeling the debilitating blows worsening, Germaine attempted to get away as Armande relented for a few seconds in order to acquire a firmer grasp of the broom. Seething with rage, Armande, hands firmly grasping the broom handle, struck Germaine on the shoulders as she attempted to flee, sending her flying into the feeding troughs, where she fell facedown to the ground. As she tried to quickly scramble to her feet, Armande continued hitting her savagely. Clutching the barn wall in an attempt to hold her body up, Germaine endured the beating until she succumbed to the brutalizing blows, and then dropped to the ground like a rag. From her mouth she softly whispered, as if it were her last breath: "I forgive…my Lord, I forgive."

Armande froze, shocked by the child's gentle whisper to heaven. For a moment, her broom held high above her head, Armande suddenly saw purity in Germaine; her eyes softened as she looked down at the child. But, very abruptly, Armande's perspective changed as she sensed being duped by another of Germaine's ruses.

"You cry to our Lord?" Armande exclaimed with rage. "Do you not know that Jesus does not help wicked children? The Lord is with me in my punishment of you. You are not a holy child; you are sheer misery and ineptitude. You failed in your duties. Did I not give you work to do in the barn? And so why haven't you done it, you lazy, despicable thing? I have a household to run, and you make it impossible for me." Armande threw the broom on the ground exclaiming, "May God have mercy on you, Germaine, for not even He can love such a wretched and worthless piece of dirt." Armande then exited through the open barn door, shouting out, as she left, "I want these chores done by sunset." Germaine remained on the ground, whimpering in pain and fear, her face swathed in bloody scratches and bruises. Completely defeated and exhausted, she laid face down on the barn floor, crying, as blood seeped from her nose and forehead.

That evening, the Cousin barn, engulfed in a nightly silence, was gently caressed by an autumn moon, which shone through the window, bathing Germaine in its light as she prayed, "O my Lord Jesus, please help me to forgive and to love. I give you all my suffering." Germaine, her head bowed low to the ground, in a deep prayer of supplication, was suddenly showered with celestial light, her entire body immersed with an angelic shimmer. Germaine lifted her head and looked around, searching for the source of the light. Suddenly, her eyes fell upon an incredible figure, standing before her. The light's intensity prevented Germaine, at first, from seeing any details, but as the light faded somewhat, Germaine could see a beautiful lady dressed just like a queen standing before her.

"Your prayer, my child, has been heard," the queen reassured Germaine. "And my son has sent me to you. He has instructed me to convey to you that the local priest, Father Jean-Granet Sabrières, will guide you along the road that will bring you closer to Jesus's most holy cross. Fear not, my child; find the priest, for it is he who will guide you. I am with you always. Will you do this, Germaine?" the regally dressed monarch gently asked.

"Yes, my queen," Germaine eagerly replied; she then hesitantly inquired, "Who is your son, my queen?"

As the apparition began to dissipate, the queen responded with a tender voice that gradually waned: "It is Jesus."

The apparition ceased and the light flooding the barn completely dispelled. From a distance, the Cousin barn could be seen lighting up the darkness. Villagers traveling the road in the direction of Pibrac could see, but for a moment, the light. As they looked on, they wondered what they had seen, and so rumors began to circulate about Germaine, but many did not believe.

The next morning, Germaine returned to the field to shepherd her flock. It was about ten in the morning when Father Sabrières walked prayerfully by the field, carrying the ciborium to give communion to all of the shut-ins of the parish. He noticed a young girl in the distance herding the sheep. He stopped for a moment and decided to walk in her direction, not knowing it was Germaine. "Hey there, little girl!" he called aloud. "Come here! I need to speak to you," shouted the priest while waving his left arm in the air to attract her attention. However, Germaine continued to look toward the sheep, attentively spinning the wool given to her by her stepmother. Father Sabrières finally reached Germaine, who was engrossed with her work.

"Little girl! Little girl! What is your name?" the priest inquired, for he still did not yet recognize her because her head was covered.

She turned and answered with extreme shyness, "Germaine, mon père." She attempted to hide her face still swollen, cut, and bruised by the previous evening's beating.

"Ah yes! You are Laurent Cousin's little girl. Why haven't you been regularly coming to catechesis on Sunday afternoons?" asked Father Jean. "Don't you desire to get to know the Lord, my child?"

"Oh! Yes, Father. I desire to know Him and serve Him with all of my heart," Germaine replied with honest sincerity.

"Well then, Germaine, it is important that you come to catechism class on Sunday afternoons with the other children. You are soon going to be old enough to be receiving communion in a few years. I need to be preparing you to receive our Lord. Shall I see you there next week, then?" he politely asked the girl.

"Yes, Father, I will ask papa and maman to take me," replied Germaine convincingly. Father Sabrières smiled gently at her as he turned away to continue his visits of the shut-ins. He knew that her father was not committed to his daughter's catechesis. *It's going to be a bit of struggle to keep Laurent in tow*, he thought to himself.

Germaine let down the hood and scarf that were covering her facial wounds once the priest had turned away. Her face lit up, revealing the profound joy that flooded her spirit, at the prospect of learning more about Jesus.

In the Cousin home that evening, the family was sitting around the dinner table eating in silence. Germaine softly knocked on the door, hoping to ask her father for permission to go to catechism classes on Sunday afternoon.

Laurent got up to answer the door. "Who is there?"

"It's me, papa, Germaine," she replied hesitantly.

"Well, come in, Germaine, but stay at the door," instructed Laurent rather coldly. "What would you like?" asked Laurent.

"I would very much like to take communion in a few years. Father Sabrières says that I will be soon old enough. He would like me to go to catechism more often, to prepare for communion. Remember, he thought that would be good for me to attend on Sunday afternoons, a while back. Don't you remember, papa? Could I, please?" supplicated Germaine with eagerness and resolve. Laurent looked over in the direction of Armande, who gave him a look of disapproval.

"Germaine, you do not know how to read, and besides, you have chores," Laurent answered with equal resolve. "Knowing how to read is so important when you are learning your catechism. Germaine, neither are you smart enough nor do you have even the most basic reading skills to be able to learn your catechism."

Armande pointedly interjected: "You are nine years old and you can certainly wait a little longer to take communion, I should think. Besides, communion is for those who have a strong faith, and that is certainly not your case."

"Anyway," continued Laurent, "you have chores to do on Sundays, and this business about learning your catechism will get in the way of your responsibilities; isn't that right, Germaine?"

"Oui, papa," answered Germaine, her face saddened by her father's answer. In the background, Loyse and Françoise giggled with each other as they looked at Germaine contemptuously. Germaine noticed Françoise's eyes were darkened, her skin gray as ash. Something didn't look right, but she dared not speak for fear of reprisal.

Sunday mass came to an end. Father Guillaume Carrière gave the final blessing, and the faithful exited the church prayerfully. The Cousin family geared up to return to the farm. Germaine squeezed her way past her siblings and Armande to get to her papa.

"Papa, can I speak to Father Guillaume for just a moment? May I?" reverently inquired Germaine.

"Of course, Germaine, but go quickly," warned Laurent.

"Thank you! I won't be more than a minute," assured the little shepherdess.

Germaine wanted to let Father Guillaume know that she did not get permission to attend catechesis in the afternoon. She hoped that he would convey the message to Father Sabrières. She fumbled her way through the pews and rushed over to where a crowd of people surrounded Father Carrière. Armande, frustrated by the delay, turned to Laurent and gave him a look of annoyance. "Now we will have to wait for her."

Father Carrière was talking with a woman about her husband's illness. Several other men and women waited patiently to talk to him, and in the back of the crowd Germaine stood, head down and patiently waiting.

As he slowly made his way from one parishioner to the next, Germaine grew more and more anxious as she waited for Father

Carrière, who had not taken notice of her. She looked back and forth between her impatient family, waiting outside the church doors, and Father Carrière chatting with what seemed like an endless stream of parishioners. *Would he soon have time to speak with me?* she pondered.

Finally, Germaine decided to push forward, knowing that if she did not, she would lose her chance.

Father Carrière was speaking with an older gentleman about cushions for the pews, when Germaine suddenly interrupted him with great reluctance and with a pitiable voice, "Excuse me, Father. Could I speak with you?"

Father Guillaume, slightly taken aback by the interruption, turned towards her to respond. However, seeing the sores on her neck leaking onto her clothes, and experiencing the nauseating odor that emanated from the seepage, he quickly attempted to hide his disgust.

"Child, can't you see I am speaking with someone else right now?" he quickly interjected while regaining his composure.

"Yes, I'm sorry, Father, it's just that—"

"You must wait your turn like everybody else," Father Carrière cut in, adding: "Patience is a virtue." The priest continued talking with the gentleman about the cushions.

"Yes, Father," Germaine agreed, bowing her head as she returned to the back of the line. Raising her head, she noticed Armande standing just inside the church door, looking in her direction with a fierce expression on her face that frightened her. The rest of the family was waiting just outside. Armande suddenly began waving for Germaine to come quickly as

Françoise, still very tired from the flu symptoms, needed to get home to rest. Pressed, Germaine yelled out from the line, "Father Guillaume, please let Father Sabrières know that I cannot go to catechism class on Sundays." She then quickly left the church.

Father Guillaume suddenly lifted his head, annoyed by the disturbance, before reengaging his interrupted conversation.

By the time the Cousins family reached their farm, Françoise had broken out in a high fever. She was shivering and convulsing by the time Laurent had carried her up to bed. Armande began immediately to sponge her forehead with cold water, hoping to control the fever. After one hour, when it was clear that her condition was worsening, Armande yelled out: "Laurent, hurry and get the doctor. Françoise's fever is not breaking; we must do something quickly." Laurent put on his coat and hat, and was already getting the horses harnessed for the wagon trip into town. It was about 2.5 kilometer away, so he knew he had little time to spare. He drove the horses hard, hoping to make good time; however, just as he was approaching the intersection with Chemin de la Fontaine, his wheel hit a crevasse in the road and the wagon toppled, throwing Laurent onto the road where he rolled several times from the impact before coming to a stop, facedown in the dirt. He was scratched and bruised but not hurt. As he slowly got up, uncertain of whether he was injured, Laurent began to ponder the seriousness of the delay created by the accident. He ran in the direction of the doctor's office hoping to ride back to the house with him. As he arrived, the waiting room was empty and there was no sign of the doctor. He ran from house to house searching for the doctor, assuming he was doing home visits, but to no avail. Meanwhile at home, Françoise had slipped into a coma after several hours of convulsions.

Finally, Laurent located Dr. Baillet at Monsieur Villeneuve's house caring for Mme Antoinette Villeneuve's grippe. By the time they reached the Cousin home, Armande had lost all hope. Upon entering, Dr. Baillet went to work, quickly trying to diagnose Françoise's condition. It took but ten minutes before he lifted his head, his eyes serious and concerned. Wiping his brow with his handkerchief, he looked at both Armande and Laurent for what seemed like a long time, and said: "Laurent, I am afraid it is an advanced case of brain fever." He paused, trying to find a gentle and thoughtful way to deliver his prognosis. He continued: "Françoise has very little time to live, Laurent. It would be best to get a priest quickly. She is not long for this world." Armande's face turned dark; her body, tense and rigid, began to flay about violently, tearing from the walls the dishes, pots, and pans that were within her grasp. She shrieked with a voice that would have terrified even the dead, and then finally collapsed to the floor, crying uncontrollably. It was clear to Armande that Germaine would, again, pay a heavy price.

That night, while Father Guillaume Carrière was preparing for his nightly divine office, he could not shake the revolting image that was stuck in his head from last Sunday's encounter with

Germaine Cousin. Those large, purulent abscesses on her neck that were now encroaching on her cheek were repulsive. He was sorry that Father Sabrières invited her to catechism class on Sunday afternoons. *Her presence in the classroom would be disruptive to the other children*, he thought to himself as he was preparing to open his prayer missal.

Father Guillaume was devoted to being an inspiring catechesis instructor, and he certainly believed that, in preparing a soul for holy communion, the soul must be, through grace and instruction, inspired to seek holiness; this is a wholesome goal, a virtuous pursuit that could only be reached by having, first, a deep hatred of sin. And so, the accepted norm, in preparing a child for communion, is to initiate them to the sacrament of confession once they have reached the age of reason. Confession becomes, then, the tool by which the children understand the importance of cultivating an internal life through a frequent examination of conscience. Candidates for first communion are supposed to be inspired to thrive to imitate holiness in their lives. And so it was on that very point that the vicious rumors circulating about Germaine Cousin troubled Father Guillaume. Louise Facet made sure the rumor mill of Pibrac ran hot and on overtime regarding the reprehensible behaviors of the little shepherdess that were reported to her by the stepmother, Armande Cousin. *This child can't just come to catechesis, if, in her life, there is not hatred of sin*, he thought. Everything he was hearing led him to believe that she was a little devil with outward piety.

The next morning, at the Cousin farm, Armande was in the kitchen putting porridge into wooden bowls for her last remaining child.

"Loyse, get down here this instant. You must eat before beginning your lessons," yelled Armande with authority. At that moment, Germaine walked in the house with a bucket of water. She put it down just inside the door and began to eye the porridge, which looked delicious. Then, as if to prolong her stay in proximity of the good food, Germaine asked, "Is Loyse starting her lessons today?"

"Not that it is any of your concern, but yes, she is," noted Armande with condescension. "The summer season has ended, and so it is time to begin school."

"Will I also be attending?" inquired Germaine with a disarming simplicity.

Armande laughed. "Ha! Ha! Ha! You! Going to school? Of course not! You are too stupid for school. You will be doing what you always do, tending sheep, weaving, and keeping the barn clean. That takes enough of your time as it is. Now, here, take your bread." Armande slammed the bread on the table. "Now go to the pasture with your sheep."

"Oui, madame," replied Germaine with deep sorrow in her heart as she left the house with bread in hand, closing the door behind her.

"Loyse! I'm not going to call for you again!" yelled Armande, as she turned away from the door. Germaine headed out to Manaut pasture with her sheep surrounding her.

The next Sunday after mass, Germaine made her way through the crowd to Father Sabrières, who had just finished celebrating mass. He spoke with some children about reverence in a church, and especially in front of the tabernacle. Then, turning around, he addressed Madame de la Croix, who had been trying to interrupt his interaction with the children,

"Madame de la Croix, Jesus reminds us to let the little children come to Him. Let us not obstruct children that need guidance," he kindly instructed the persistent woman.

"You are right, Father. It's just that Jacques is in so much trouble, and I don't want to disturb things," she replied with a deeply concerned voice.

"It is natural to not want to disturb, madame, but you must be patient, and you must endure in your prayers for him," he wisely counseled.

Germaine, with more determination than her last attempt to speak with Father Guillaume, squeezed up in front, right next to Father Sabrières. Madame de la Croix, feeling the child's insistence, backed away, saying, "Thank you, Father, for assisting me."

"Pray, madame, that the Lord may guide you," exclaimed Father Sabrières.

"What can I do for you, little girl?" asked the pastor, now finally liberated from the daunting requests of the many women.

"Oh, excuse me, Father, I must speak with you. It's very important Father," insisted Germaine, fearing the loss of Father Sabrières's attention.

"Yes, I'm sure it is," acknowledged Father Sabrières, who finally recognized Germaine, despite the scrofula sores spreading over part of her cheek and significantly disfiguring her.

"But I am very, very busy right now, Germaine. I have confession, and then I have some very important business to attend to," replied the priest.

"But, Father…," the little shepherdess interjected, with disappointment written over her face. "I just want to let you know that I won't be attending catechism classes anymore."

"Ah, I see; and why not?"

"My papa did not give me permission," answered Germaine with disarming honesty. "I tried to let Father Guillaume know last week. I had hoped that he would tell you," the little shepherdess admitted.

"Ah! Is that so! I will speak with Father Guillaume, and with your parents!" the priest reassured the little girl.

Germaine's face lit up with hope. "Oh, thank you, Father. Thank you," Germaine repeated with exuberance, as she left to rejoin her parents and sister, who impatiently waited in the carriage.

Not a week had passed that Father Sabrières made arrangements to meet with Laurent Cousin in his office.

"Now, Laurent," said Father Sabrières, "I insist that you let your child prepare for first communion. It is my responsibility to ensure that the youth of the parish complete the sacraments as they mature. She needs confession and communion as she has reached the age of reason."

"But, Father, my child is as stupid as an ox. She cannot read or write, and she is ill all the time," replied Laurent defensively.

"You send her to the pastures with the sheep every day…do you not?" inquired the priest.

"Well…yes, I do…but…," replied Laurent. However, his ability to further defend himself was abruptly cut off by the priest.

"So, then," inquired Jean-Granet Sabrières, "does she not complete full days without complaint?"

"She does," Laurent admitted, his head bowed in shame, before attempting a rebuttal. "But Father, I—"

"I shall entertain no excuses in this matter," the pastor quickly interrupted. "She deserves the Lord's instructions and graces. I will expect to see her next Sunday, after mass in the afternoon, without fault," the priest insisted with a regal tone of authority, which Laurent knew not to contest.

"She will be there, Father!" Laurent replied with resignation.

The following Sunday, the children were all sitting in rows on the floor at catechism class, listening to Father Guillaume Carrière's lesson. Germaine had a pitiable demeanor but an attentive look as Father Carrière taught the lesson. Because of her repulsive neck sores, she knew disgusted the other children, Germaine remained at the back of the room.

"So then, my children, why does God allow suffering?" the priest inquired with interest.

Father Guillaume Carrière looked around the classroom as the students stared downward, hoping he wouldn't ask them specifically. His eyes scrutinized each face. Finally, his gaze came upon little Jeanne Marchand, positive this was one of those children with a deep desire for holiness. *She is beautiful and attentive, her eyes clear and pure*, he thought.

"You, Jeanne, why do you think God allows suffering?"

"Father, truly I do not know," the child responded with a perplexed look on her face.

Father Guillaume continued to look around the classroom. His eyes came upon Germaine, sitting in the back of the room; she was lowly, dressed in rags, her face slightly disfigured by the bruises from Armande's beating the night before, and from the scrofula sores leaking from her neck and face. She was repulsive, and Father Carrière could not bring himself to invite her into the discussion.

He turned instead in the direction of little Jacques Morneau; he was eleven years old, and a little gentleman if there ever was one; always joyful, funny, and full of little tricks to scare the girls with. He remembered that this kid was much like him when he was but a toddler. He looked directly at the boy. "Jacques, why do you think God allows suffering?"

"O Father, I don't know; it doesn't make any sense to me." Wanting to put Germaine on the spot, because he disliked her so, he continued: "Ask Germaine, I believe she knows."

Father Guillaume reluctantly faced Germaine and asked: "Why does God allow mankind to suffer, Germaine?"

She lifted her head, paused for a moment, surprised she was being spoken to; collecting her thoughts, she responded, "So that He can draw from that suffering a greater good."

"That was answered well," the priest exclaimed. He continued, "But what does this mean, my children, to suffer so that God can bring a greater good?"

Lucie Villeneuve, one of the adolescents of the group, chimed in, "Because He loves us, He does everything for us?"

"Certainly, love is the center of God's being, but is there something more?" the priest patiently inquired.

A silence filled the room. *What more could there be?* thought Jacques Morneau. The priest waited for some kind of reply. He turned in the direction of Lucie Villeneuve, who was always ready for a challenge, but she could not respond. The priest then scanned the class, as a whole, looking for a response. Father Guillaume's face grimaced, but for an instant, as he contemplated asking Germaine. He turned to her, her face disfigured, her countenance wretched, and asked the little shepherdess. And so she replied, "Suffering is given to us as a way the Lord can test our love for Him. He can see if we really love Him, when we are patient in our suffering and never seek to abandon Him at the cross."

"That is partly right, child. So then tell me, Germaine, how does any good come from suffering?"

Looking at the priest, her eyes visibly thoughtful, she replied, "I am not sure, Father."

"Then how is it that you know that being patient in suffering is important?" inquired the priest.

"You taught us at mass, some weeks ago, how important it was to patiently give our suffering to Jesus, and that He would use our suffering to do good things…as long as we were patient. You said something about letting go of our suffering." She paused, quietly bowed her head, and remained silent for an instant, before looking up and saying: "You said we had to die. I did not understand, but then you read from the Bible: Jesus said, 'Amen! Amen! I say to you, unless a grain of wheat falls to the ground and dies, it remains just a grain of wheat; but if it dies, it produces much fruit. Whoever loves his life loses it, and whoever hates his life, in this world, will preserve it for eternal life.' Then, I began to understand," answered Germaine, calmly and peacefully, as if pondering the significance of each word.

Father Carrière was stunned by Germaine's perfect understanding of the question, and of her excellent recitation of scripture. *How could a stupid child with such a grotesque appearance have this kind of knowledge and memory of scripture without ever having been to school? Is this all a ruse by a conniving child with devious intent?* he wondered.

"You have answered well, Germaine," replied the priest. He continued Germaine's explanation: "My children, like the grain of wheat, we must die, but to our own selfish desires. The great mystery behind dying to ourselves is revealed to us as we are able to approach the most holy cross of Jesus; this is a lesson frequently taught by Father Sabrières."

Father Carrière continued, "My children, it is time to go, the catechism lesson is over. I will see you next Sunday." The children filed out of the classroom as the priest gathered his belongings. Germaine was the last to make it out the door.

Father Carrière looked at Germaine as she was leaving. His lips hesitantly opened, as if prepared to call out her name, but he stopped himself, looking at her with intrigue as she walked barefoot out into the cold, only meager rags covering her body.

Months had passed, and every week Germaine attended catechism classes. At the back of the room she sat, deplorable in appearance, poor and disfigured, listening to the religious teachings, collecting deep within her heart every word and every fragrance of love that she heard, like precious dewdrops from heaven. In turn, Father Guillaume, dumbfounded by the incongruity between the child's pitiable appearance and her understanding and memory of scripture, grew in amazement of the child's spiritual growth. In April of that year, after many weeks of catechetical instruction, the children left the parish office for the last time; they were now ready for first communion.

He looked on as Germaine left, her ways so lowly, simple, and unassuming. Her deformity and disease caused in him a revulsion that was difficult to contain. He then remembered the scriptural passage from Isaiah 53, which he whispered softly to himself as if to reinforce his own faith and realign his thinking towards that of the greater divine mystery:

Despised, and the most abject of men, a man of sorrows, and acquainted with infirmity: and his look was as it were hidden and despised, whereupon we esteemed him not.

O my Lord, the assistant pastor thought to himself. "I was blind, O Lord, but now I see," the good priest repeated with sorrow, as he understood how it was that his earthly eyes could not see the great beauty hidden within the rags. Germaine exited the church, her ration of bread tucked away under her arm.

The next day, following Germaine's first communion, Father Sabrières, after he had said daily mass and was walking from the sanctuary through the church, noticed Germaine kneeling in a small side chapel. She was intently praying, her face staring at a large crucifix hanging on the wall. He approached her with a concerned face and said, "My child, something is troubling you…what is it?"

"Oh, Father, I am not troubled, it's just that I desire, now more than ever, to know how to approach Jesus's holy cross," Germaine revealed. She continued, "Father Guillaume talked about this at catechesis one Sunday, but I do not know that road; can you show me?"

"You wish to approach the cross?" Father Sabrières thoughtfully inquired. "Yes, the cross," Father Sabrières repeated to himself, thinking it unusual that a child would make such a request. Once again he solemnly repeated, "The cross," as if preparing to enter a chamber of hidden mysteries. He then continued, "My child, to get closer to the cross we must learn to submit to what the Lord sends our way. We must look upon our afflictions as blessing from God, not some kind of injustice. Germaine, you can never trust our Lord too much; indeed, because we know that God's goodness and mercy are infinite, we should then have infinite trust in Jesus. It is wise to remember, Germaine, that when times are difficult and dark, not to hesitate to love and throw yourself into Jesus's arms, because it pleases Jesus to know that we need Him so much. He likes that we confide in Him, and rely so much on His tenderness and love. In fact, the poorer we are, Germaine, the more we have a right to His caresses and His graces," explained Father Sabrières most joyfully.

"Oh, Father! How I wish to trust more and to love more," exclaimed Germaine with complete trust.

"Then love the Lord in return. Surrender to His will for you. Come to morning mass if you can, Germaine." He paused and reflected, then continued. "In any event, Germaine, you are only a child…there is no need to get close to that cross quite yet. Simply trust in God, and Jesus will lead you along the road He desires for you," cautioned Jean-Granet Sabrières, who had trouble understanding the child's zeal. "You must go now, my child, or you will be late for supper."

Germaine replied, "But, Father, my papa would need to give me permission to attend daily mass; he would never agree to this; that, I am most certain, as I have my sheep to care for." Father Jean prayerfully replied, "Then ask this favor from God and trust He will grant it to you. Now, go on your way, or you will be late."

The next day, Germaine walked down the road on her way to the pasture with the sheep in tow. It was a quiet and calm day as there were not many on the road yet. The sun bathed the countryside in a fresh luminescent hue. As Germaine neared the Manaut pasture, she saw Bernard sitting under a tree. He leaned over his knees, an empty bottle in his right hand. Bernard sang some inaudible song that she could not hear. Germaine approached Bernard, playfully saying, "Bonjour, Monsieur Bernard! Are you well?"

Coming out of a stupor and slurring his words, he said to her, "Bonjour, young maiden. I am well, and you?"

Germaine, sensing that something was wrong with Bernard, said to him, "Bernard, you don't seem well…Are you ill?"

"No, my dear, I'm a sinner; I'm not ill. In fact, I feel just fine, but I am a sinner and you, as pure as you are, shouldn't look at me." Bernard's hands and arms covered his face.

Germaine said in reply, "Oh, Bernard, you are a silly man! I'm delighted to see you as always. But whatever the matter is, I think you should eat some of the bread that I have for you. Here, take some." Germaine handed Bernard one of the scraps of bread she had for her lunch. Bernard took it gently, with great appreciation.

"Oh, thank you, mademoiselle," he said with gratitude and gentleness, adding, "You truly are a saint, a little saint in the making."

Germaine replied with a concerned look on her face, "Well, that ought to make you feel better. And perhaps you should sleep more. Most people aren't even awake yet." She had great pity in her sweet little voice.

"That sounds like a good idea; thank you, child!" Bernard responded reverently. "Say a prayer for me. You'll do that, won't you?" he kidded as he got up and began to head down the dirt road toward Pibrac.

"I will," responded Germaine as she guided her twenty or so sheep in the direction of the Manaut pasture.

By late afternoon, Bernard, sound asleep and snoring under a burlap bag in an alley adjacent to Pibrac's town center, was awakened with a startle to the sound of a horse whinnying as it pulled a carriage through the street. It was Monsieur Facet and his two daughters, Lorre and Marguerite, fourteen and seventeen years old respectively. Jean Facet turned to his daughters as the carriage approached the marketplace, and said, "I'm sorry to take you out of your lessons, girls, but your mother is not well enough to get out and do this, and I certainly don't know the first thing about cooking food."

Marguerite turned to her father and asked, "Is she very ill, papa?"

"No, she is not ill at all," he replied with clear frustration in his voice.

"Then why is she in bed so much?" Marguerite asked. Her father replied, "My dear, I'm not sure what to tell you. She says she has headaches, but the doctor can't see why. She claims to be tired, but how can that be when she is sleeping all day?"

"O papa!" Marguerite exclaimed, putting her hand on her father's shoulder.

"I'm sorry, my dears; maman just needs our help right now, is all; she is just overworked," Facet gently explained.

Lorre suddenly piped up, "I'll help as much as I can, papa."

"I will too," Marguerite promptly joined in. "Things will be fine. You'll see, papa."

"I know they will, thanks to you girls," he reluctantly admitted. He knew full well that his sexual escapades with Claire Leguard was the true reason for his wife's sickly demeanor.

They suddenly came to a stop near the market's food carts.

"Now here is the list your mother gave me. I am giving you thirty sous…so now go and find the items your maman needs. I have some business in town. I'll meet you back here in an hour," instructed Jean.

"Oui, papa," Marguerite and Lorre joyfully replied in unison.

"Good girls," Jean acknowledged, and then took off down the street, while his daughters looked over their mother's ingredient list.

Meanwhile, unbeknownst to Germaine, Loyse, now fifteen years old, had been watching Germaine from a behind a bush in the woods bordering the pasture, hoping to play a trick on her. As Germaine began down the path in the direction of Manaut pasture, the sheep surrounding her as she walked,

Loyse slowly came out from behind the shrubs and followed her, always maintaining a safe distance to avoid being seen. When she arrived at the pasture, Germaine took her usual post just partway down the ridge, and there she sat, watching over the sheep. Loyse, hidden behind a rock some thirty feet away, began to observe Germaine closely; she grabbed a rock in her hands, hoping to scare her by throwing the rock into the nearby woods. Germaine took out her old string rosary, one she had made from an old discarded hay-bale cord not long after Armande had thrown out, in one of her fits of rage, the beautiful rosary her dear mother had left her. Knots replaced the beautiful beads normally found on a typical rosary, but it was all she needed to properly meditate on Jesus's passion. She then knelt down on the grass, and began to recite the rosary. Loyse, hand held high, ready to throw the stone as hard as she could, was struck by Germaine's prayerful demeanor; she especially noticed how the sheep surrounded her as if to protect her.

Suddenly, the bells of St. Mary Madeleine Catholic Church began to ring in the distance, calling the faithful to daily morning mass. Germaine, still unaware that Loyse was lurking in the nearby woods, bowed her head and asked the Lord, in prayer, permission to go to mass that morning, as Father Sabrières had instructed her to do. The Lord spoke internally to Germaine, whose humility and simplicity pleased Jesus greatly. "*My child, use your shepherd staff, raise it high toward the heavens, and plant it in the ground, and there your sheep will remain unharmed until you return. Go then in peace, knowing that your flock is protected.*" Germaine rose to her feet and did as the Lord had commanded.

She brought her staff up over her head and thrust it down into the ground despite her lame right arm. Kneeling before it as if it were a crucifix, she recited, what seemed to Loyse, a short exhortation. Crossing herself with the sign of the cross after she was finished, she rose to her feet and began to walk in the direction of the church. The sheep mysteriously gathered around the staff and continued grazing as if they could hear or see a shepherd. Remarkable, there they remained without any indication they were tempted to follow their shepherdess; none of them dispersed. Loyse, astounded by what she saw, dropped the stone to the ground, her mouth opened in awe of what she was seeing.

Once Germaine was completely out of sight, Loyse ran down the path leading to the church in Pibrac. Once in the town, she met Lorre and Marguerite shopping for food for their papa. Loyse ran straight for them and grabbed Lorre without any hesitation, saying, "Lorre, Lorre! I have to tell you something."

"Loyse! What have you seen?" Marguerite inquired with concern. "You're as pale as a ghost!"

"I have to tell Lorre something," Loyse insisted.

"What is it that is so important?" asked Marguerite, who was losing patience. Loyse quickly pulled Lorre aside and whispered something in her ear that was inaudible to Marguerite.

"Now, girls, no secrets; that's very rude," Marguerite said with a strong parental tone.

Lorre turned to Marguerite. "Can I go play with Loyse just for an hour? You don't need my help anyway, and I'll be back before you're done. I promise."

"Lorre, you know papa told you to stay with me," Marguerite wisely advised her sister.

"Please, Marguerite? Please give me permission to go?" Lorre supplicated Marguerite in a rehearsed manner, as if knowing full well that she would concede and give in.

After a moment's pause: "Oh, fine. It's easier without you anyway," Marguerite admitted, as if frustrated by the whole interaction.

"Oh! Thank you," Lorre promptly replied.

"No more than an hour," Marguerite sternly warned.

"Yes, I will be back before you know I am gone," Lorre yelled back as she was running off with Loyse.

Meanwhile, Germaine was exiting the church after daily mass with a small number of parishioners. Her eyes peaceful, but her bodily bruises still very painful. She looked around carefully for any sign of Armande before breaking from the small gathering to head back to the sheep. Many men, women, and children laughed and teased Germaine extensively as she walked by, because of her piousness and the poor rags she wore.

"Hey there, little holy truant!" yelled out one woman, trying to ridicule Germaine.

"O pious worm, where is your God?" yelled out a man.

Another interjected, "You prayerful witch, stay far way. What spell are you casting, and on whom?"

"Hey, look at the walking rag moving on the street!" one woman interjected loudly as Germaine quickly walked by, her head bowed down as if to hide her face. Children giggled and lashed out profanities at her as well.

Germaine walked with determination as she headed back to the pasture to be with her sheep. She couldn't wait to be away from the townspeople. She prayed that the Lord protect her from being afraid or ashamed of her faith. "Lord, forgive them for they know not what they are doing," she would quietly whisper to herself. Finally, she reached the pasture, where she saw her sheep huddled around her staff as the Lord had promised, but she also found two little girls, huddled in amongst them.

"Loyse? Is that you?" Germaine asked in disbelief.

Loyse stood up quickly; Lorre, overcome with fatigue, slowly followed.

"Hello, Germaine," Loyse sheepishly greeted her stepsister.

"What are you doing here? Is papa all right?" Germaine nervously inquired

"Yes, he is all right; it's nothing like that," Loyse assured Germaine.

"Oh, good," sighed Germaine, with a clear expression of relief written over her face. The two girls came out from the circle of sheep to meet her.

Loyse began to explain: "Well, I followed you here today. I wanted to see the sheep."

Germaine looked happy, but cast her eyes upon the ground as she felt Loyse's deceit.

"Well, here they are," Germaine said as she pointed at the sheep.

"Oh!" Loyse replied, hoping to conceal her real purpose.

Lorre was staring at Germaine, her eyes oddly fixated on her during the conversation. Finally, she got the nerve to walk over to Loyse and whisper in her ear.

"Hum!" said Loyse as she contemplated Lorre's request.

"Germaine?" Loyse asked.

Germaine's eyebrows furrowed, and she replied, "Yes."

Loyse continued, "Well, how is it that the sheep stayed around the staff like that? They never strayed." With her finger, Loyse pointed to the perfectly contained flock.

"I just trusted that God would protect them," replied Germaine unassumingly. The two girls looked at her with great curiosity.

Seeing they desired more of an explanation, Germaine continued: "I trusted that Jesus would not abandon the sheep…I entrusted them to Him, who is the good shepherd."

"Entrusted?" Lorre hesitantly asked.

Germaine further clarified: "I mean that I prayed that God would watch over the sheep while I went to daily mass…I trusted that He would protect them from the wolves."

"And it worked? They always stay there?" Lorre inquired with more exuberance than she wanted to divulge.

"Oh, yes. I didn't lose any sheep," Germaine assured Lorre. She smiled gently, uncertain of what to make of Loyse's sudden interest.

"Why would God listen to you?" Loyse finally inquired with an air of resentment suddenly coming to the surface.

"He listens to everyone!" answered Germaine with utter simplicity.

"He doesn't listen to me!" admitted Lorre.

"Will you tell us how to get God to listen?" asked Loyse, eager to know the secret.

"Well, I just ask our Lord! I don't think there is any special way that I know of," admitted Germaine, now perplexed by the question.

"Come on, let us know the secret? I want to make miracles happen too!" declared Loyse, whose true interests were becoming visible to Germaine.

Germaine's eyes looked to the ground, troubled by their lack of love for the Lord. Finally, as if prompted by the Holy Spirit, Germaine admitted, "I don't do miracles, Loyse." Her face looked down; her eyes saddened.

"I know I have never been very nice to you," admitted Loyse, "but I want to be your friend now. I am sad by how maman treats you so poorly, but now I can help you, if you just show me how to do miracles!" Germaine's countenance suddenly darkened as she realized Loyse's intentions.

Lorre piped up: "Just tell us about the sheep, then. Tell us how Jesus helped you go to church."

"Well, I can try."

The girls sat down in the grass amongst the sheep and Germaine attempted to explain Jesus's role in their lives as the true shepherd.

"Jesus is a good shepherd, you know, who never leaves His lambs unattended. This is because the wolves could come and scatter them, and eat them. So the good shepherd gives us angels that remain with us always. They watch over us and protect us when needed."

"Are the angels big and strong?" asked Lorre.

"Oh yes, I do believe they are, but I have not seen one! I imagine that they can be so big and strong that the wolves dare not approach the flock," said Germaine.

"Is that what He did, send you down angels from heaven?" continued Lorre.

Germaine paused, and then replied: "I don't know, but He watches over me and you as well."

Loyse listened, but a great hatred for Germaine burned in her soul, for jealousy had taken root in her heart like a weed, slowly snuffing out any charity that may have remained.

As November set in, the nights became much colder. One night, it was colder than usual. Germaine, now ten years of age, was lying down on her makeshift bed, freezing from the cold wind. Between the fourteenth and nineteenth centuries, most of Europe experienced harsh winters—historically, this period was referred to as the "mini–ice age." The night air was biting and the wind could be heard forcing its way through the slats of the barn. Finally, Germaine decided to try and sneak into the house, if only for a moment, to get a bit of warmth from the fireplace. She walked across the lawn to the gate and, in un-latching it, startled Loyse, who was lying awake, unable to sleep.

Loyse quietly got out of bed and moved across the room to the stairs. As she entered the main room she could hear the latch of the front door jiggle. She quietly approached the door and opened it. There stood Germaine huddled under a sheepskin.

Loyse, surprised to see her, invited her into the house. "Come inside quickly, Germaine, and get warm."

Germaine hesitantly came inside and stood in front of the dying fire. Grateful to Loyse for her charitable act, Germaine whispered, "Thank you. It's so cold outside."

Loyse went to get a stool and brought it over for Germaine to sit on while she warmed herself.

"Here! Sit down," Loyse insisted.

"Thank you," little Germaine responded, her lips still shivering.

"I'll boil you some water for tea to warm you up," said Loyse.

Loyse put a small log on the fire, poured some water into the pot, and placed it on the fire. The two girls sat in silence. After a long pause, Germaine said, "Thank you for being very kind to me."

"No one should have to be outside in this kind of cold," explained Loyse, whose intentions were far from pure. As Germaine sat by the fire for warmth, Loyse ran to wake up her mother, knowing full well Germaine would get in trouble for being in the house.

After being roused, Armande walked from her bedroom and entered the main floor dining area, the deep incrusted lines on her face reflecting a fury that suddenly alarmed Germaine's heart.

"What is going on in here?" Armande lashed out with obvious indignation. Loyse, who had ran back to Germaine's side, stood frozen, her face looking straight at Armande, as if she were surprised by her sudden arrival. "How dare you come in here and wake me up! Wake my daughter up! I told you, long ago, to stay in the barn at night so that my children don't become ill. Is that not what I said?"

The young girl replied, a mere whisper coated in fright emerged from her mouth, "Oui, madame, I'm so sorry. I was just getting some hot water to make tea, and warm up a little by the fire," Germaine pitiably explained. "I am so sorry I woke you."

Loyse said nothing, but just backed away into the shadowy corner of the room. She was sadistically intrigued by what her mother would do to Germaine.

Winter's harsh winds could be heard furiously whipping the side of the house.

"Hot water! Oh, was that all you needed?" Armande questioned with a falsely caring and concerned voice that reassured Germaine, but only for a moment. Then Armande's gentle voice dramatically morphed into a cruel and frightful screech, "Then by all means, Germaine, have some hot water." The stepmother took the pot of boiling water from the fire and threw its contents at Germaine, hitting her in the chest, arms, and legs. Loyse, hidden in the shadow of the stairs, let out a little scream and ran upstairs, unable to endure the torturous scene. Germaine moaned in pain, but Armande didn't give her time to make a scene. She grabbed her by the hair and threw her out the door, screaming, "You get back in that barn and don't ever let me catch you in this house again."

She slammed the door, and at that moment Laurent came out from the bedroom.

"What happened, my dear? What is going on?" asked Laurent, still half asleep.

Armande turned and headed in the direction of the bedroom, brushing her hands together, saying, "It was just a rat trying to get out of the cold. I took care of it; go back to sleep."

On the cold ground outside, Germaine was in shock, her body trembling as if she were going through an epileptic seizure. Her chest and arms burned with such indescribable pain that she gasped for air at every breath. Her mouth was wide opened as she rolled around on the ground crying and moaning. The boiling water caused blisters and redness on her chest and arms which then opened up and leaked. Her facial expression was frozen in a timeless scream that echoed through space, reaching right into heaven. She crawled on the ground until she reached the barn, and finally passed out in the hay. Numerous angels filled the interior of the barn and ministered to her while she was unconscious. Once again, travelers from Toulouse reported seeing lights glimmering from the inside of the barn while they were traveling in the dead of night. But nobody dared approach the farm.

The next morning, Germaine woke up, lying on the barn floor, ever more aware of the severe burning pain all over her body. As she saw the sun rise in the horizon, she mysteriously found the strength to get up from the ground, grab her staff, and head outside. Once she stepped into the sunlight, she moved away her cloak to take a peek at the damage the boiling water had done. Her arms were bright red, blistered and sore. She looked down the front of her dress and sighed with pain.

She then took a deep breath and, without going to the house for her bread, she gathered the sheep by calling each lamb by name, and began her trek to the pasture with the sheep following close behind her.

In church the next day, about half an hour before he celebrated mass, Father Sabrières heard Germaine's confession. As he slid the little curtain back that covered the portal, Father Sabrières began to speak: "In nomine Patris, Filii, et Spiritus Sancti! Amen." Germaine was kneeling on the other side of the confessional. After Father Sabrières's blessing, she whispered, "It has been one week since my last confession, Father."

"Trust in the Lord's mercy, and say your sins without fear," Sabrières enjoined her.

"Oh! Father, for a brief moment, I was filled with such despair, and stopped trusting in Jesus when my stepmother threw hot boiling water on my legs and tummy! It hurt so much that I cried…I complained to my Lord…I am so sorry, Father, for my sin of mistrust."

Father Sabrières, shocked by what he heard, remained speechless for a brief instant. He then replied, "The Lord Jesus suffers with you, Germaine, but He does allow this suffering to take place. As you cried and felt you were alone and abandoned, so also did Jesus weep, but right beside you did He stand. It was in this distress that He was closest to you. This was a sin against God, for He forbids that such abuse should take place."

As if to clarify, and to hold on to what she understood the priest had said, she further asked, "You mean He is there, close to me?"

Father Sabrières paused again for a moment in order to collect his thoughts. "Yes, child, the Lord is watching over you and assisting you with His angels, though you are unaware of their presences," Sabrières assured her. He continued, "The suffering the Lord permits is much like a burning fire which purifies; the greater and more intense the flames, and the more frequently that He plunges you into the crucible, the greater the purification and the benefit to you. The Lord is not happy with the way you were treated, Germaine, but you must know that His love is perfect in every way, for indeed, He has great love for your stepmother. Trust in Him, and pray for the conversion of your stepmother." The priest knew that the confessional seal prevented him from confronting her parents; he had to remain silent in the face of the abuses. He too would pray for the stepmother and for Germaine especially.

That evening, the Cousin family was seated around the supper table. They ate in silence as they listened to furious winds thrashing over the roof and through the surrounding trees. Germaine was in the barn, hidden and huddled under sheepskins, trying to keep warm. The Cousins, comfortably sitting around the table, knew of Germaine's plight, yet nobody spoke about her. Armande's overbearing presence stifled any attempts at raising any concerns about her well-being.

Laurent remained silent because he was weak, and unable, and unwilling to stand up to his wife. Armande's matriarchal reign was supreme in the Cousin household. There was no question about who ruled the nest. The loss of Anne and Françoise was too difficult to endure for everyone, but especially for Armande, who now had to deal with Loyse's declining health. It appeared that Françoise's brain fever was likely contagious.

That night, perhaps because of the frightful cold winds, Laurent struggled with the injustice directed at Germaine. While Armande lay in bed, Laurent, pacing back and forth, finally voiced his concerns:

"Armande, my darling, surely you must recognize that it is too cold for a child, for any man, to sleep outside. The wind itself would be enough to cause grave harm to anyone."

"Laurent, don't be so dramatic," Armande cautioned her husband. "Grave harm, you say? Do you know what grave harm is? It is my children dying from some hideous skin disease that they acquired because of your daughter contaminating them. That is very grave, Laurent; I have lost Anne, and then the Almighty chose to also whisk away Françoise not long after. Besides, in the barn, Germaine has layers upon layers of sheepskins out there. She has a bed with a blanket, and so she is perfectly fine. The thing is not suffering by any stretch of the imagination. Besides," Armande reassured her husband, "the cold helps contain the infection. I have told you this many times already."

Laurent persisted. "But Armande, are you sure of this?"

"Laurent, of course I am," Armande insisted. "It is best for her and for us. Now there will be no further conversation. I've taken my medicine, and I'm now going to sleep."

On a nearby road, a husband and wife from Pibrac were riding by the Cousin home on a horse and carriage. The woman turned to the husband, "Is that not the Cousin farm?"

"Yes, I believe it is," the man responded.

"Stop the horses," the woman commanded. Instantly, the man pulled on the reins to bring the carriage to a stop.

"What is it?" the husband demanded, concerned that he had just averted tragedy.

The woman rubbed her eyes in disbelief and inquired, "Is that a light coming from the barn? It's so bright; I've never seen anything like it."

"I believe it is," replied the husband, also astounded by the mysterious sight.

"It is their farm; I remember now," pondered aloud the wife. Laurent and Armande are the parents of that pious impostor, Germaine? She is the one with those horrible abscesses on her face that many say are an evil curse."

He and his wife got out of the carriage and approached the farm cautiously; they peered into the barn and saw Germaine kneeling in deep prayer before a makeshift altar, immersed in a bright light that appeared to be warming and comforting her; she was unaware of their presence. The couple's eyes and mouths were wide open in awe. Suddenly, as if they had become fully aware of the sacred and mystical nature of their vision, the couple turned away, frightened that they may be disturbing a very holy event. Quickly, they both got back in their carriage and rode away in haste. The story ran like wildfire through Pibrac, many choosing not to believe because of the many disparaging stories Armande had circulated about her stepdaughter. This couple, however, was not so quick to believe the nefarious rumors about the little shepherdess.

It was 1594, and the winter came early that year, blanketing the region with patches of snow; Germaine was now fifteen years old. One cold afternoon in November, the sun was high, and Germaine was standing amongst her sheep. Five children were also there with her, listening attentively to her as she shared with them stories of Jesus's love. They were children from some of the poorest homes of Pibrac and of the outlying region.

"Jesus is a good shepherd," she reminded the children. "He never abandons His sheep, even when the wolves approach. If they are in trouble, Jesus sends His holy angels to protect them. For you who are His little sheep, Jesus also protects in the same way. He sends His angels to watch over you, but first you must be faithful to the Father's word, and mustn't be shy to ask for protection. The Lord is generous to those who are faithful to Him; Jesus wants you to ask great things of Him. There is nothing the Lord cannot do…ask the Lord with faith, and be persistent with your prayers," Germaine enjoined them.

"Oh yes! We will, Germaine," the children joyfully agreed. "Will you show us how to pray now? Pray with us," the children entreated her. The children gather around Germaine and knelt on the ground, eagerly waiting for further instructions.

Germaine took out her corded rosary, which she always kept in the right pocket of her apron. She then began, "I will recite the sorrowful mysteries of the rosary; they will help us meditate on the Lord's passion…His suffering. In the name of the Father and of the Son and of the Holy Ghost, amen! I believe in God the Father, almighty creator of heaven and earth, I believe in Jesus Christ…" Her voice faded in the wind that swirled around the eager youth, who persisted in prayer right until the end of the sorrowful mysteries. Soon after, as the children were getting ready to depart, Germaine reached into her apron, and drawing from her meager ration of bread, she gave the children what appeared to be generous morsels, for she knew they were hungry. Afterwards, they began to depart for their respective homes. Germaine, in the midst of the field and surrounded by her sheep, remained kneeling, peacefully in prayer, oblivious to time and weather, until the sun began to set. The temperature suddenly dropped from the seasonal 13 degrees to 5 degrees centigrade, the low normally reached in a typical November evening. And so Germaine wrapped her feet in rags she always carried with her, especially for days when the cold was too much for her shoeless feet to endure. It was time to head back to the farm, and so Germaine called out the names of all her sheep, diligently ensuring that none had wandered off.

Darkness had already covered the French countryside of the township of Léguevin by the time Germaine reached the barn. Wind had also picked up and began to sweep the fields. Pibrac was in the region of the Midi-Pyrénées, situated at an altitude of about 590 feet above sea level, and so wind intensity could be stubbornly persistent and stronger than in lower-lying regions. Germaine wrapped herself in a sheepskin blanket, as she expected the temperatures to drop below freezing. She lit a small candle on her makeshift altar, and knelt before pieces of wood she had bound together to form a crucifix. "Please don't let me get too cold or too hungry tonight, my Lord," she whispered ever so gently, and then bowed heard reverently.

That week, her confession with Father Sabrières had been most helpful in bringing her soul closer to Christ. After admitting to her fears of being too cold and hungry, Father Jean, understanding Germaine's soul after these many years, and suspecting the depth of suffering Christ wished to bring her through, said, "Why, O Germaine! Why do you uselessly resist the chastisements of God? Do you not realize that He is your true father? Do you not understand that He strikes us for the sole purpose of detaching us from the miserable pleasures, worries, and preoccupations of this world that separate us from Him? What greater favor could Jesus accord us that would do more to deliver us from our useless attachments to those things that could ultimately prevent our spiritual combustion from being complete? Do you not wish to be changed into fire, Germaine? That is, into holy fire? Do you not desire the divine penetration to be so complete that your soul may burn more thoroughly?"

"Oh! But I do, Father Jean. I desire this with my whole soul," replied Germaine.

"Then allow your soul to be deified; or rather, transformed into this fire of love." Father Jean paused for a moment, and internally invoked the Holy Spirit to guide his council so that it be consistent with the Lord's most holy will. He then continued, "At first, Germaine, the soul can burn but a little with this love, but to love completely and totally, the fire must penetrate into the deep recesses of the soul. This can only be accomplished through a divinely ordained purification, which allows the divine fire to penetrate and possess the soul more deeply. Years ago, Germaine, you were convinced that your mother's death, your isolation in the barn, and separation from your family were great misfortunes. How you grieved and suffered, but yet, you were able to see with time that this was indeed far from being the case. You have, in fact, learned to die to all the world's allures, temptations in the direction of pride, sentimentality, and charms, and to give glory to God for the Lord's most joyful providential strokes of love. So then, Germaine, you should strive to see that Christ's divine action is actually concealed, so that you must be silent and still, to see it deep within you, acting around you and through your actions."

"But, Father!" Germaine protested. "How shall I know that my actions are God's will? Oh! How I fear displeasing our Lord, most of all," Germaine admitted.

Father Sabrières smiled behind the confessional curtain, realizing and sensing the young girl's sanctity, then answered her with pause and serenity, "The degree to which you love is the measure you should use, Germaine, in discerning if it is God's will. Fear not, for you will be confirmed in your actions to the extent that you love. And so, Germaine, believe the Lord will guide you, and your prayers will be answered according this love."

Germaine, mystified by the priest's instruction, inquired: "But, Father, how should I know the degree of love that it is in my heart?"

The priest, his eyes closed, his head bowed, looked deep within his soul for the guidance he now needed to provide this precious flower, this pure lamb. He answered, grace abundantly filling him, and, *in persona Christi*, the state in which all priests become the earthly Christ who forgives and guides, he said, "In discerning the extent to which this love possesses you, ask of our Lord that if this action or that prayer be pleasing to Him, that your soul may burn with a fire of love so intense that you may know with certainty, that if it were not for his providential protection, it would surely consume you."

Germaine, wanting to more fully understand the beauty of this surrender and the mystery of God's internal fire of love, then asked, "Father, I want to understand more completely what you are saying to me. Can you please, I beg you, explain more?"

Father Sabrières closed his eyes, uncertain of how to proceed. He suddenly understood that now was the time for silence and reflection. He feared turning his counsel into an intellectual diatribe that risked suffocating the soul rather than enlightening it. He reflected for a moment, *confusion is always the outcome when too many words are spoken.* "Germaine, no more needs to be said for now. You already understand more than you realize." He directed her to say her act of contrition, gave her absolution, and charged her with a short penance. She left the church after completing her penitential prayers, and then quietly returned to her sheep.

Manaut pasture was lovely in the springtime and a short distance from the shepherdess's home. Germaine was now sixteen years of age. She continued to accommodate her duty of shepherdess with joy, and was always determined to do her very best. She diligently watched over the sheep and kept them safe, and spun her assigned bundles of wool the days she wasn't sick and worn down by either the heat of summer or the cold of winter. Every day she continued to entrust her sheep to the Lord so that she may attend daily mass. Since Loyse had passed away over the winter, Armande was ever more vengeful in her verbal and physical attacks on Germaine.

Despite the continued abuse, Germaine found the time and the charity to share her pitiable daily rations of bread with the poor and destitute homeless who travelled the roadsides of the diocese, looking for food, work, and some shelter. Abundant were the families during that time that lived in indigence. Indeed, by the mid-sixteenth century two important social phenomena became vectors of heightened societal misery: the first, was that population growth was significant enough during the fifteenth and sixteenth centuries to match fourteenth century pre-plague population levels, leading once again to higher unemployment; the second, was that inflationary price hikes had made food more expensive and less accessible to the common folk, a reality that got further amplified by salaries not keeping up with this inflationary surge, causing many families to have limited access to nutritious foods.

Germaine would reach into her apron and pull out pieces of bread to feed the many poor that traveled the countryside. Often the Lord would multiply the bread for her so that she would never run out. All those who came to her never left hungry.

Tuesday afternoon, Germaine had completed her duties early, and saw from afar a homeless family making its way along the roadside. They approached her, having heard stories about her charity.

"Here, monsieur, I have but a few fragments of bread to share with you," she humbly stated, so as not to falsely raise the father's hopes. "Are these your children?" she inquired. "Here, I have a little more for them too," she gently assured him.

"Oh! Thank you, mademoiselle." He paused, his eyes looking toward the ground in shame. "You are so kind. Yes, this is my family: my wife, Madeleine, and my three children, Marie, Jean, and Marie-Eve. We are grateful for your bread...we have not eaten in two days." Overwhelmed by the young maiden's generosity and holiness, he fell to his knees before

Germaine and kissed her feet. His wife and children knelt behind him and bowed their heads in thanksgiving to the Lord for this beacon of light. He rose to his feet, and looking at her, said, as if to further emphasize his appreciation, "Again, *merci*!" He turned and walked away, giving the morsels of bread to his children and then to his wife. More homeless travelers could be seen approaching in the distance, and yet, despite being hungry, Germaine's face lit up with joy, as she saw the opportunity to help others who, she perceived, were in greater distress than her. Reaching into her apron, she found that more bread was available to assist the needy.

In late afternoon, the very next day, the market was bustling with men and women making their daily purchases of commodities and produce. Armande was mingling among the ladies at the fruit stand. Among them were Louise Facet, Madame Jeanne Baillet, the wife of Pibrac's medical doctor; and Madame Isabelle Champin, who was the wife of Joseph Champin, the town's baker. They all listened with intent to Armande's disparaging accounts of Germaine. "If you only knew, ladies, if you only knew! She is the pious one from the exterior, but a lying thief in practice, I assure you. There is nothing holy about this devil of a child!"

"Oh my!" exclaimed Isabelle Champin, who was standing by Louise Facet. "Many of our children go out to the field to spend time with her in the afternoons. Should we be concerned?" she fearfully inquired.

"Is that so? So she entertains visitors?" Armande cynically exclaimed. "Why would they possibly want to be out there for?"

"I suppose they are having fun playing games. That's probably why her work is often unfinished," Armande said with vindictiveness clearly reflected in her hard expression. "You do know the child is cursed. Those unsightly sores on her neck and face are most certainly signs of the demonic. I warn you now, ladies, this stepdaughter of mine may curse your children also, and then with her stories of demons and ghosts, enslave them to fear and anxiety. You cannot possibly want this for your children. Be assured that they are not safe as long as they are around her."

"Well, I don't know about the others, but I am putting an end to my daughter's visits to that devil of a child," Jeanne Baillet admitted. "My own daughter has been going up to the pasture to see Germaine along with other children, almost every day. I was convinced that Germaine was an innocent and pure child; what a deception!"

"Germaine and my daughter Claire spend nearly every afternoon up there," exclaimed Isabelle Champin. "Claire says that Germaine tells her and the others about Jesus, Mary, Joseph, and the angels. It all sounds pretty innocent to me!"

"My own children go up there all the time and sit with her for hours so that they can hear her beautiful stories about the saints," another woman in the market interjected.

Armande, her face bewildered by Isabelle Champin's reflection, replied, "Do not be deceived by the child, my dear Isabelle, for she likely fills the children's heads with not only foolish stories and ideas that cannot be formative for your children, but with supernatural fables of ghosts and witches that are dangerous to their souls."

Isabelle Champin gasped in horror, her mouth opened, her hands clasping her face. "Dear God protect us," she cried out.

"If I were you, madame, I would forbid your child from spending time with Germaine. I tell you, Germaine is not to be trusted with your children," Armande sternly warned.

"My children have assured me that she tells them good and beautiful stories; how terrible can that be?" Madame Gauthier interrupted; she was the wife of Alfred Gauthier, the town's prosecutor. "Germaine appears to be harmless, Madame Cousin. I see no harm here! Not in my children anyway. There may be even some good coming from those visits."

"No," Armande shouted with insistence and alarm. "You don't know what she's like. That girl does not deserve an audience for her fantasy stories, her dark imaginings. You should tell the other parents not to let their children visit Germaine. She is working and does not need any distractions."

"I, for one, am not allowing my little Jacqueline to return to visit that holy impostor. If her mother insists that she is a dangerous influence on other children, then who am I to oppose her," replied Madame Normandin.

"I say leave her alone, Armande!" enjoined Madeleine Gauthier. "I don't see any evidence that my children are being harmed by Germaine. Besides, Manaut pasture is a safe haven for the children. It is not wolf-infested like La Bouconne forest. Did you hear that Monsieur Bossuet lost several sheep yesterday in the field near La Bouconne, and his shepherd, André, was savagely mauled by several wolves?"

Madame Lacombe, who was purchasing potatoes and parsnips, overheard the conversation. "Oh my Lord!" she exclaimed. "This is tragic. I thought there were no more wolves around Pibrac."

Isabelle Champin, who had not budged from Louise Facet's side, added, "This is very recent, my dear. It was also clear to me that there were no more wolves. My husband says that packs of wolves have been getting nearer because the last two winters have been particularly harsh, leaving the wolves hungry and without fear of humans."

Armande, who by now had become quiet, listened to the ladies discuss the reasons for the wolf infestation, her eyes severe and dark, deviously plotting Germaine's demise. Then Armande suddenly spoke up, "In any event, I will put an end to this matter of children distracting Germaine; this girl has disobeyed me for the last time."

Louise Facet, concerned by Armande's vindictive and vengeful tone, quickly spoke up, "Calm down, Armande!"

Furious by the news that Germaine was spending her afternoons entertaining other children with fantastic imaginary stories, Armande vociferously lashed out, "What? Calm down? I have had enough of that child torturing the name and dignity of our Lord with fairy tales and dark stories of witches. Why, she may even be causing other children to sin against God!"

"What are you going to do, Armande?" inquired Jeanne Baillet, her voice reverberating with concern. Armande, her eyes

locked on Jeanne Baillet, were fierce with anger, but she spoke
not one more word.

That night, Germaine was drawn out of her sleep by shouting
coming from the house. She suddenly sat up in her bed and,
listening closely, understood she was in trouble again. She could
hear Armande's voice yelling out her name. Germaine knew
that Armande intended to punish her severely for something;
she could not, however, decipher the reason. Frightened and
terror-stricken she fell to her knees and begged the Lord to
help her endure the pain for love of souls and the conversion
of her stepmother's wicked heart. "Oh! My sweet Jesus, help
me to endure this punishment in reparation for my offenses,
and those of my family, and especially for the conversion of my
maman's cruel heart."

Armande rushed into the barn like a diabolical whirlwind,
her fury, like a Vesuvian tempest, gave the impression it was
about to annihilate everything in its path. "How dare you incite
other children to sin by disobeying me? You wretched creature!
You will pay dearly for your obstinacy. You fill the heads of the
children with fantasies and lies. You are deranged and unworthy
of God's protection. You little deceitful saint! Who will protect
you now?"

Armande, broom in hand, flipped the broom around,
and proceeded to strike the little shepherd with her broom

handle with such force that the handle snapped as it struck Germaine's back.

Germaine, projected off her feet by the force of the blow, flew into the barn wall. On the ground, Germaine lay motionless, her eyes opened in terror, her forehead bleeding profusely. With a voice seething with anger and hate, Armande instructed, "From now on you will take the sheep to a new pasture. Starting tomorrow, you will go to La Bouconne forest where the pasture is lush."

When Armande left, Germaine slowly sat up, bleeding and seriously bruised. The little shepherd painfully crawled along the floor in the direction of her little altar. Painfully getting on her knees, she began to pray, her makeshift rosary beads flowing through her hands.

The very next day, Armande promptly made arrangements to meet with Father Guillaume in the church rectory.

"Father I have come to you as a matter of conscience," Armande admitted with an exaggerated pious demeanor.

"What exactly is troubling you, Madame Cousin?" inquired Father Guillaume.

"I have been careless, Father, with my own child. I recently found out, through a friend, that children have been visiting my stepdaughter, Germaine, while she worked in the pasture. It's there, in the field, away from any adult supervision, that she has been scandalizing other children with fantastic fables that she dreams up and that cause spiritual harm to other children. I have not been vigilant about what she does when watching the sheep. I am horrified, Father, by the stories she tells. O Father, I have grievously sinned by not carefully and dutifully instructing and guiding her," Armande complained.

"This does not necessarily make you careless," Father Guillaume cautiously and calmly explained.

"Father, had I paid more attention to what my stepdaughter was doing in Manaut pasture, I would have been able to put a stop to this right away."

Father Guillaume, suspecting a ruse, asked in reply, "You would have put a stop to what, exactly, Madame Cousin? To the stories or the other children visiting her in the pasture?"

"To both," Armande replied with tears flowing profusely. "Oh, Father, if you only knew Germaine. Yes, I know she seems like a perfectly respectable and pious child from afar, but I tell you, she is not what she appears to be. She has many defects, one of which is lying, and she is a very obstinate liar at that. I'm concern about how these stories could cause a loss of faith in other children," explained Armande, who was getting agitated.

"What are these stories about, Madame Cousin?" quietly asked father Guillaume, who was struggling to discern the authenticity of her emotional displays.

"Father, she speaks of angelic beings, muses, witches, and demons that walk about the countryside. The children become alarmed and fearful; I am concern about the scandal it brings to innocent ears."

"Oh! My goodness," replied the priest, his concern all of a sudden peaked. "And what exactly, are your daughter's other defects, Madame Cousin?"

"Oh, Father, the list is long and troubling. I hate to even get into this here. Though, I do suppose Germaine's behavior is part of why I accuse myself of being careless. To think that innocent children such as little Françoise and Anne could have been scandalized by Germaine's lies and stealing, when they were alive. Oh my Lord...the deceit causes the soul to quiver," Armande disquietly explained.

"Stealing, you say?" Father Guillaume exclaimed, looking for confirmation.

"Oh yes, Father. It is so sad really. The girl, despite getting more than generous daily portions of food, steals bread from the household all the time. I'm afraid she has some very negative compulsions. She shows hardly any virtue, Father. I know she goes about like a little pious saint, but, Father Guillaume, I want to assure you that she is nothing but deceit. It is all appearances; nothing is real. Laurent and I do not know what to do!" Armande sighed in discouragement.

"The strain on the family can be significant and difficult to bear," said Father Guillaume, now suspecting the story to be true.

"Thank you for understanding, Father, but what should I do?" inquired Armande, her face perplexed.

"Above all things, you must correct her, punish her severely when you see these deceitful behaviors. Then pray for her; the Lord always hears the prayers of caring parents," Father Guillaume counseled, and then, remaining pensive for a moment, added, "Father Sabrières seemed to have taken some interest in her, a while back, when he visited the catechism class on Sundays. I must admit that I also have been impressed by her."

"Father, you should speak with him about Germaine," Armande cautioned.

"Perhaps someone ought to before she makes a fool of him and all of us. I will speak to Father Sabrières privately," Father Guillaume assured Armande.

8

The Lord Protects His Sheep

*Nothing happens in this world that is not according
to the decrees of Providence who turns all things to the
advantage and greater profit of souls that are submissive
and resigned.*

—Father Jean Pierre de Caussade (1675 –1751)

Jean Facet tenderly kissed Claire Leguard as they departed
from one another. They had been secretly meeting in the
mornings to make love after the children left for school. It
was the most convenient time, now that his wife, Louise, had
decided to visit her sick aunt for a few weeks. Their torrid love
affair was like a whirlwind, passionately tossing them about with
emotions and desires they had never experienced before. This
was the love she had always desired; the intimacy, the physical

pleasure was beyond her imagination. This seemed so right, and yet, guilt internally ate away at her. Their affair had been going on for eleven years already, and neither of them wanted to end the encounters. But Jean was married, and so was she; this was the reality, and the truth that seemed to burden mostly her. Jean could see that she was troubled and needed reassurance.

"I love you, Claire; don't be so agitated. Louise has been visiting her sick aunt in Toulouse, and will likely not return until another six days," Jean convincingly reassured her. The affair had been going on long enough that uncertainty and guilt frequently threatened the relationship.

"She knows you're being unfaithful," Claire exclaimed.

"How could she possibly know that? We've been very discreet. There is no way she could know," Jean Facet said nervously. "Louise is always sick with something," he retorted. "I can't stand it; I have needs, and I will be damned if I have to wait for her to be well."

"It is because of her illness that we met and fell in love. We shouldn't really complain, should we?" pointed out Claire.

"I suppose not," Jean responded, and then paused. "You should go now, so that I can go to work."

"Yes, yes; time to go," Claire mechanically repeated, as she prepared to leave.

"You will come next Thursday?" Jean inquired.

Playfully, Claire replied, "We'll see," as she vanished out the door.

Claire Leguard quickly walked across the property in the direction of the wooded path that led to town. Soon after, as she was far into the woods, Marguerite, Jean's daughter, came running down the path, paying no mind to Louise Leguard. In reaction, Louise pulled her hood over her head, and walked more quickly in the direction of town. Marguerite ran across the yard towards the house and rushed through the door. Jean Facet was pouring himself coffee.

"Papa, you need to go get Lorre. She is at La Bouconne forest with the Cousin girl; you know! The shepherdess, Germaine. Maman says that there are dangerous wolves out there. Come, papa, hurry!" Marguerite shouted.

"Calm down, child. What exactly are you talking about?" the soft-spoken father asked calmly. "I thought you were at school."

"O papa! Maman doesn't want her up there playing with the Cousin girl…you know…the one who is all scarred and ugly. She won't listen to me, and with maman visiting Aunt Violette, I don't know what to do…You have to come and get her and bring her to school, papa!" Marguerite insisted.

"Very well," Facet submitted. "What is all the fuss about her playing with this Cousin girl, anyway?"

"It's rumored that she is speaking about the devil up there, and poisoning the minds of the children," Marguerite explained, the concern still visible on her face and in her voice.

"What children?" asked Jean, who still did not fully understand.

"She always has a group of them up there. Maman said Lorre can't be up there, papa. Plus, maman says there are wolves where Germaine brings her flock. It could be very dangerous."

"All right," conceded Jean. "Let me get my coat." He put on his coat and boots, and then followed Marguerite out the door, all the way to the pasture.

Germaine and Lorre had been walking for some time in the direction of the church to attend daily mass. Between the path and the church itself was a large creek commonly known as Le Courbet. Usually the waters were very shallow, allowing Germaine to routinely skip across the creek to get to the other side in order to attend mass in the morning. This particular morning, however, the water was running very high as the spring runoff and abundant rains made the creek run fast and deep, making it impassable. Meanwhile, Marguerite and her father, Jean Facet, were running in the direction of the pasture located near La Bouconne forest, only to find the sheep gathered around Germaine's staff as if shepherded by an invisible angel. Germaine and Lorre were nowhere to be found.

The children of the town normally enjoyed teasing Germaine every morning as she dutifully walked to St. Mary Magdalene Church. Today, they thought it would be particularly amusing to ridicule her as she faced the impassable Courbet creek. All of the children, gathered along the Courbet before school, chided Germaine for her homeliness and prayerful ways from the other side of the creek. They dared her to cross.

"O holy one! Let Jesus walk you across the waters. Ha! Ha! Ha!" Laughter abounded and persisted. "O pious one, you will need to walk on the waters to get to mass today? Ask your Jesus to assist you." Still more laughter came from the mouths of the irreverent youth.

Lorre, in attempting to defend Germaine, drummed up enough courage and yelled back at the children, saying, "Stop calling her names; leave her alone." Immediately, she turned to Germaine, held on to her left arm and said, "Don't try and cross, Germaine, the waters are too deep and fast!"

Germaine, filled with the Holy Spirit, and trusting in God as a lamb trusts its shepherd, gently unlatched Lorre's hand, and spoke with serenity, "God will find a way for me to cross, if He desires me to be at mass."

Lorre, concerned that Germaine was walking to her death, replied in desperation, "No, Germaine, it's too dangerous."

Internally, Germaine prayed, "Dear God, I must get to mass on time. Show me the way across this water. I trust infinitely in your love, O Father in heaven."

Meanwhile, Marguerite and her father, while running over the top of the hill, saw the children by the river.

"Oh dear God. No, Lorre, get away from the waters," Jean yelled. The children could not hear Jean Facet yelling from the distant hillside, as the raging waters drowned out his voice. Jean started running down the hill, with Marguerite following close behind; his intention was to save the children from a calamitous end. As Germaine finished her prayer, an internal locution guided her: "*Like my prophet Moses before you, pick up the stick that is at your feet and raise it above your head, and cross the Courbet with faith.*" She raised the long stick above her head, then stepped forward, no fear, anxiety, or distress impeding her trust in Jesus.

Lorre yelled out one more time, "No, Germaine!"

As she stepped from the bank, the water miraculously parted before her. Once her foot hit the rocky bottom of the river, she could see a perfectly straight path to the other side, the waters forming a wall on either side of her. The children gasped in awe as she made her way through the waters without ever getting wet. Up on the hill, Jean and Marguerite, halted in their tracks, their eyes wide open in amazement, were unable to comprehend the incredible sight; it was a miracle to behold, the likes of which they had never seen, and likely never to witness again.

"My God, she is an angel," exclaimed Jean Facet. Overwhelmed with emotion, he broke down and sobbed bitterly; falling to his knees, his conscience suddenly accusing him of his sin of adultery. He continued sobbing for several hours, there, on the side of the hill, leading to the Courbet. Marguerite, by his side, sought to blindly comfort him, for she knew not of her father's unfaithfulness.

The crowd on the other side of the Courbet remained silent and astonished at what they witnessed. The once pugnacious youth that leveled insults at Germaine had also fallen to their knees, their own conscience troubled by their ridicule of the holy young shepherdess, and by their blasphemy against God. As Germaine walked by the boys and girls who had been silenced by their own grief and contrition, Germaine lifted the staff high above her head, so that the many irreverent children would bow their heads to the ground in acknowledgment of God's incredible power. Then thrusting it into the earth, she in turn bowed and knelt before it as the others raised their heads and looked on. She then stood up and walked to mass, many of the youth silently following behind her.

Father Jean-Granet Sabrières was heading out for the evening when Father Guillaume stopped him. "Father, I'd like to speak to you, for a moment, if I could?"

"What is it, Father Guillaume?" inquired Father Sabrières.

"It's regarding the Cousin girl," replied Father Guillaume.

"What is it that concerns you?"

"I understand you have become protective of the little Germaine girl," suggested Father Guillaume.

"Tell me, what preoccupies you?" inquired Father Sabrières.

"Well, I don't believe that the pious behavior you have seen in the girl is necessarily honest and true. It may surprise you to find out that she is nothing close to what she appears to be. Her own mother, Armande Cousin, confirmed that the girl is nothing less than a liar and a conniving thief."

"You know, Father Guillaume, that discernment in these matters is very, very important. I gather you have already judged and condemned the child?" asked Father Sabrières.

"Of course not, Father. It's just that I'm worried that you may be misled by this impostor."

"Father Guillaume, I have heard your concerns. Was there anything else?" respectively inquired Father Sabrières.

"No, nothing comes to mind," answered Father Carrière sheepishly.

"Very well then, I still have my office to recite, so will you excuse me?" asked Jean-Granet Sabrières.

"Most certainly, Father Sabrières," replied Guillaume Carrière, as he watched the pastor leave the church.

Jean Facet and Claire Leguard stood facing each other in the woods.

"I cannot go on living in sin like this. God sees all that we do, and to ignore Him is to call divine justice upon our heads, and I can no longer afford to do that," Jean Facet bitterly confessed to Claire Leguard.

"But I love you," protested Claire.

"This is not love. I have a duty towards my children and wife; that is love. Love is a decision, not a feeling, Claire; we were both misled. I'm sorry, I must go now," Jean replied, an unbearable grief exuding from every pore.

"What has happened to you?" asked Claire, her voice laced with concern and alarm.

"I saw an angel today, and instantly, I witnessed the sordid state of my soul," he answered. He left her there, in the woods alone, and walked home to his family.

Pibrac's town hall was slowly filling up. Father Guillaume Carrière and Father Jehan Hoguet sat at a table, set up in the front of the hall, preparing to preside over the meeting. Germaine had become the talk of the town since the parting of the Courbet; many of the townspeople of Pibrac were concerned about the mystical occurrences that surrounded her. It did not help matters that Armande Cousin was in attendance, her malicious mouth speaking ill of Germaine, and fueling alarm among the fifty or so citizens that had gathered. Father Guillaume brought the meeting to order, amidst unsettling shouts and arguments about the shepherdess.

"We need to keep that girl away from our children!" yelled out one young mother, concerned about Germaine poisoning the minds of her own little children. Another woman disclosed, "My daughter sometimes spends all day with her, and now her flock is close to the wolf-infested Bouconne Forest. It's too dangerous for the children to be there."

Father Hoguet motioned with his hand for everyone to calm down.

Father Guillaume pleaded with them, "There will be time to hear everyone's concerns and opinions, but we must keep things orderly."

"You have sat on your hands long enough! Our children are in danger of being scandalized by this charlatan girl; she might even be a witch," one man piped up.

"What is she teaching the children?" another concerned woman inquired.

Madame Montreuil, the wife of the town barrister answered in defense of Germaine, "She tells the children Bible stories, and speaks of angels; surely there is nothing wrong with this?"

"Well, she is free to spread the word of God. Perhaps more of you need to evangelize others, just as Germaine is doing," Father Guillaume said with a tone that was beginning to show impatience. Father Hoguet pridefully turned and, facing Father Guillaume, his eyes piercing and his face painted in a sort of ecclesiastical arrogance, said, "I believe the word is ours to spread. We have spent years in seminary, and she can't even read!"

"It's her fault anyway," the town apothecary blurted out as he pointed his finger in the direction of Armande Cousin. "The truant belongs to Armande, and she needs to take care of this."

Armande stared at the man, her glacial eyes peering vindictively into his soul as if casting a curse upon him. "Excuse me?" she finally said. "Do you dare question my efforts and intentions?"

"It's your fault the girl has taken hold of the hearts and minds of our children," the man forcefully explained.

"Yes! If you could only raise your child properly she wouldn't be such a menace," the town seamstress responded.

"She is NOT my child!" Armande shouted in protest. Then with a softer voice, steeped in false pretense, she continued, "She is a burden. A burden I did not ask for. But it is one I bear because that is what God has chosen for me." She paused a moment, looking around the room for a sympathetic eye, and then shouted out in an accusatory tone, "If anyone is to blame for this, it is Father Sabrières; he has taken Germaine as some sort of protégée!"

"Yes, I think we can all agree that Father Sabrières may be fueling the fire," Father Hoguet interrupted.

Suddenly the door to the town meeting hall opened abruptly, and Father Sabrières walked in, his presence imbued with sanctity and grace. Silence, suddenly overtook the meeting room.

"Am I interrupting?" Father Sabrières inquired with an authority that caused some in the crowd to stir uncomfortably.

"No, of course not; I mean, not at all," Father Hoguet quickly, but hesitantly, responded.

Father Sabrières walked towards the front of the hall where the other priests were seated. The people watched him as he passed through the crowd, his eyes fixed on the two presiding priests.

"I was unaware there was a meeting. What are we discussing?" he asked with what seemed like genuine interest.

"Well...the Cousin girl," Father Hoguet sheepishly admitted.

"And why are you having this discussion?" asked Jean-Granet Sabrières, hoping to get to the bottom of this assembly's intentions.

Father Carrière, sensing trouble, finally admitted, "We're concerned about Germaine Cousin's rather negative influence on the children of the community."

"I see," Father Sabrières coldly responded. Reaching the front of the room, he then turned in the direction of the crowd and looked at them for a moment. His eyes, it seemed, peered into each individual soul.

"Do you realize that all of these people are here as concerned parents, troubled by the events surrounding Germaine?" questioned Father Guillaume.

"And what events might you be referring to?" Father Sabrières asked, his eyes fixated on the crowd.

"She is talking to the children about witches and ghosts, and other times, spreading the word of God. Armande Cousin, her mother, attests that Germaine steals bread from the household to feed vagrant travelers. She lies about it, and influences children to lie and disobey their parents," Guillaume Carrière explained. "Why, there are even rumors that she is a witch. In fact, just the other day she parted the waters of the Courbet, just like Moses did; how can a child perform such wonders, lest she be a witch? Think about it! This kind of wonder can only be diabolical," the priest exclaimed, lifting his hand to heaven as if to punctuate the incredibility of the stories. "We must put an end to this before she starts raising the dead," explained Father Carrière.

Father Sabrières, his right eyebrow raised, kept his accusatory eyes locked on the people. He cleared his throat, after pondering the discourse he had just heard, and said with a righteous air, "This strikes me as pure gossip. You should all be ashamed of yourselves. Germaine's trust is visibly with God and not demons; it does not surprise me to hear that she is feeding the poor and preaching the word of God to the other children. You should all be doing the same, you who have so much more than

193

her. I say shame on you for accusing such an innocent soul. You should be all educating your children in the faith. The way I see it, that little shepherdess is doing your work. Further, the accusations that she speaks of witches and performs diabolical wonders are to be discounted. Nothing of the sort could ever come from that child's mouth or actions."

Father Jehan Hoguet, feeling that he was about to lose the support of the townspeople, replied, "Father Sabrières, you must understand, we cannot allow the uneducated to preach, nor can we permit witchcraft to take place in our town; our complaisance might be misinterpreted."

One of the town merchants came to Father Hoguet's defense. "It is not that we want to condemn this child; it's just that our children seem to have more faith in what Germaine Cousin says than in what they hear from the pulpit."

"Trust me, my good people," Father Sabrières pleaded earnestly, "what Germaine is saying is what you all hear in church. The fact that she is helping your children relate to it should make you happy. It is a grace not given to many." Looking out of the corner of his eye in the direction of the other priests, he continued, "If she is willing to share with your children that which she learned from the catechism that was taught to her Sunday afternoons, then you must thank her, not condemn her."

"But Armande has assured us that the girl is a liar and an impostor," Father Hoguet interjected, trying to regain the support of the people.

"This is true," chimed in Father Guillaume.

"Yes, many times, I've heard that she steals and has no respect for her parents," continued Father Hoguet.

"Armande, is this true?" Father Sabrières cried out, looking for clarification from her stepmother, the only one who could confirm these rumors. Armande, however, was nowhere to be found. She had snuck out at the very moment Father Sabrières arrived.

"People, listen to me. You have every right to do what you please with your children. As parents, that is up to you. But I will not support a social and religious persecution under my watch, especially of one so innocent who is spreading the word of God. Have your children been spouting blasphemy since spending time with Germaine? Have they begun to steal or to lie?" the good priest inquired.

The crowd remained silent. Sabrières continued, "Then return to your homes and speak of this no more. I expect to see many of you in the confessional for participating in this public display of gossip and character assassination." He looked around the room, paused, and then pronounced, "This meeting is adjourned." He then left as swiftly as he arrived. The crowd, dumbfounded, proceeded to quietly leave.

The next day, the town square was filled with villagers going about their daily business. As the church bells rang out with their twelve-noon chimes, many of the townspeople knelt and prayed the Angelus. This practice was common throughout France at that time.

Up near La Bouconne forest, Germaine, upon hearing the bells, also knelt down and began to recite the Angelus. As she did, three wolves, seeing an easy prey, began approaching from a distance. Moving slowly through the trees, the creatures remained hidden in the shadows of the woods, their menacing presence concealed from Germaine, who was unaware of the pending danger.

Germaine bowed down and solemnly recited, "The angel of the Lord declared to Mary and she conceived of the Holy Spirit. Hail Mary, full of grace, the Lord is with thee. Blessed art thou among women and blessed is the fruit of thy womb, Jesus. Holy Mary, Mother of God, pray for us sinners, now and at the hour of our death, Amen. Behold the handmaid of the Lord; be it done to me according to thy word." As the wolves got closer, Germaine, still unaware of their presence, prayed harder for Armande's conversion, "Hail Mary, full of grace, the Lord is with thee; blessed art thou among women and blessed is the fruit of thy womb, Jesus. Holy Mary, Mother of God, pray for us sinners, now and at the hour of our death. Amen."

Hidden behind the trees, children and adults alike, gathered more numerously and frequently, to witness the mystical phenomena that surrounded her. Believers, nonbelievers, heretics, and secular intellectuals were getting wind of the unusual events surrounding the young maiden. So, propelled by curiosity or tainted with cynicism, they hid themselves behind trees and rocks so that they may get a better glimpse of the shepherdess. But often, as is the case when approaching fire, upon seeing her or getting too near to her, like flies, they fell to the ground, her sanctity compelling many into repentance, conversion, and full submission to the Lord.

As the wolves got nearer, the crowd became alarmed, some were prepared to intervene. As they pounced to attack Germaine, something stopped them in their tracks. They looked up past Germaine to see a very large figure in the distance, holding a massive sword. It was Michael the archangel. Only the wolves and some of the observers, nestled among the trees, could see the archangel, who stood, enormous in stature, some fifty feet away from the prayerful Germaine.

Meanwhile, the little shepherdess continued, oblivious of the wolves' threat, "And the word was made flesh: and dwelt among us. Hail Mary, full of grace, the Lord is with thee; blessed art thou among women and blessed is the fruit of thy womb, Jesus. Holy Mary, Mother of God, pray for us sinners, now and at the hour of our death. Amen."

The wolves were frozen, almost mesmerized by the enormity of the angel. Michael, in all his wondrous glory, stood nearly thirty to forty feet in height, with beautiful black hair hanging down on to his broad shoulders. He was dressed in a white linen tunic and sandals, and around his waist was a rope. He held a thirty-foot sword in both hands and began to raise it above his head.

Nevertheless, Germaine, ignorant of the mystical phenomena surrounding her, continued the Angelus, "Pour forth, we beseech thee, O Lord, thy grace into our hearts; that we, to whom the incarnation of Christ, thy Son, was made known by the message of an angel, may His Passion and Cross be brought to the glory of His Resurrection, through the same Christ, our Lord. Amen."

As Germaine finished her prayer, Michael brought his sword down, thrusting it into the ground with such strength, that it created vibrations in the earth powerful enough to cause the wolves to yelp and whimper as they eagerly scurried into the woods. Startled, Germaine, who was reciting the "Amen," turned to see the wolves running away from her. She then frantically looked all around her, and just out of the corner of her eye she caught a glimpse of a very large flash of light as the archangel vanished.

Germaine closed her eyes in great serenity and did the sign of the cross to complete the Angelus, after which she stood up and returned to her sheep. Alone on the hill, a large but gentle gust of wind blew over her. Her face reflected the physical sufferings and the fatigue of a long day. The clusters of observers, peppering the hillside, began to disband, fearful of approaching Germaine, but anxious to return to town to recount what they had seen, and mindful of heading right to confession afterward, for many had been leading very sinful lives.

Germaine walked with the sheep across the pasture. She enjoyed being alone and doing the work of a shepherdess. She heard wolves howling from the woods, and began to pray amongst the sheep.

The winter had settled on the country that year with a fierce and unforgiving grip. It snowed more than in previous years, but it was the cold, biting as it was, that made it difficult for Germaine to endure her long days tending the sheep. Her feet, by this time, were unprotected, her shoes having fallen apart years before. She regularly led the sheep barefoot through the countryside, enduring the cold the best she could. Over time, the thick calluses that had built up under her feet attenuated somewhat the crippling sharp edges of the stones and pebbles her poor feet endured on the way to the pasture. She often wrapped her feet, on the colder days, with old rags she would take from the barn, but on this particular day, the cold was fierce and her bruised, discolored feet, though tightly wrapped in old, doubly thick cloth, were no match for the frightful cold that swept across the valley. It was a suffering she gladly accepted now that she understood the great merit she could earn by offering the suffering for the conversion of sinners; most pressing to her was the conversion of her stepmother. She was so thankful for the spiritual guidance given her by Father Sabrières; his words gave her such hope. On one occasion, she remembered that the priest had wisely taught: *All things are governed by providential decree, nothing happens without the Lord's permission. But be sure of this, Germaine, this providence can also transform these things that appear terrible into something that, in the end, profits the souls who submit and resigned themselves completely to the Lord's will.*

By the time she reached the pasture adjacent to La Bouconne forest, Germaine rested for a moment while she tightened the cloths that wrapped her tender feet. Her toes, swollen and bluish, were bleeding. She held on to her feet as if to squeeze life back into them, but all she could feel was a burning sensation and numbness. She closed her eyes and prayed:

"My Jesus, help me not to be too cold or hungry today," her sweet voice gently whispered to heaven.

With some difficulty, she stood up and led the sheep to the middle of the pasture. There, they settled and began to nibble on the grass poking through the new-fallen snow. Suddenly, the wind began to blow with greater intensity, and Germaine's clothes were clearly insufficient to protect her from the penetrating chill. *Is it possible to endure this frightful cold much longer?* she thought. Moving about helped manage the burning sensation on her feet and the chill penetrating her bones. So she walked to and fro for a while, keeping her little sheep within eyesight. However, the cold that day was so bighting that she could no longer overcome the pain. Crouching down on the ground she tried to cover her feet as best she could with her garments, but feeling that her efforts were fruitless, she resorted to prayer.

"Perhaps today I will die, my Lord. Into your hands, O Lord, I commit my soul. May your will be done," the young shepherdess whispered with exhaustion.

She got back up and attempted to move in the direction of the hillside, where she had planned to watch the sheep from a higher ground. As she endeavored to tread across the frozen field, Germaine rolled on the ground, in an attempt to provide some relief to her frozen feet. However, somewhere amidst the shivering, prayers, snowfall, and the wind, she began to feel an extreme exhaustion taking over her as she lay there on the ground, large flakes of snow covering her body; like a seductive temptress, sleep began summoning her in a most persistent manner. *I mustn't fall asleep. Armande will punish me*, the poor shepherdess reminded herself, as she feverishly tried to get back up. Her efforts were in vain, as consciousness soon faded, her tired and weakened body finally surrendering to sleep.

Suddenly, from the woods emerged a pack of wolves, their movements predatory, their postures, hostile; they could smell an easy prey, and so advanced swiftly but covertly. Looking down hungrily at the sheep, the leader picked up on an opportunity as he could not see any shepherd. Promptly, he called to his pack, which eagerly surrounding him within seconds, hungry for the hunt. The pack leader, the largest of the wolves, surveyed the scene and saw Germaine's motionless body lying in the snow. As the pack approached her body, the leader moved forward, drawing nearer to the girl, his predatory instincts heightened. St. Michael the archangel, visibly present by her side, his sword and shield clearly evident, caused the wolf to cower to the ground, recognizing the superior entity from a previous encounter. The wolf avoided the angel's glance, keeping his head directed towards the ground, remembering the terrifying look the angel had cast upon him when he first attempted to attack Germaine, several weeks before. The instinct to run had been deadened, replaced instead by a submissive crouch that forced his jaw to the ground. At the slightest gesture of this mighty angelic warrior, the leader, with his entire pack behind him, crept forward, moving no longer in the direction of a prey but rather toward a precious, freezing child at the silent command of the angel. As animals do in severe cold, they gathered together, tightly huddled, to conserve warmth. In an exceptional way, however, they enclosed the unconscious shepherdess in their midst, in order to tightly cuddle her with their warm bodies. The wolves took turns on the outside of the circle to form a shield so as to bear the brunt of the wind.

The leader, the one who should have led the kill, instead took up his place at Germaine's feet, his jaw to the ground directly beside her frostbitten toes. To no one did this predatory beast ever submit but here, at the helpless little girl's feet. It was at the silent command of the angel that this normally dominant pack leader met his match. Instead of devouring the girl and her sheep, he instead lay still, and with his very breath warmed her feet. The child laid still, absorbed by a sleep so profound, that she lost complete awareness of her surroundings. The wolves remained with her until moments before she awoke, at which point they quickly scattered into the woods, freed from the angelic power.

9

Expect Great Things from the Lord

"From them that resist thy right hand keep me, as the apple of thy eye. Protect me under the shadow of thy wings. From the face of the wicked who have afflicted me."

—Psalm 17:8–9 (Douay-Rheims Bible)

And you shall be hated by all men for my name's sake: but he that shall persevere unto the end, he shall be saved.

—Matthew 10:22 (Douay-Rheims Bible)

Germaine, now nineteen years of age, had established a regular habit of attending daily mass and weekly confessions with Father Sabrières. On one such occasion, in the summer of 1599, she entered the confessional and waited for the curtain to open before unloading her soul of the burden of sin her examination of conscience had accused her of. "Father, I have sinned. It has been one week since my last confession," the shepherdess admitted.

The good priest responded, "Trust in the Lord's mercy."

Germaine continued, "Father, I have failed to do all of my duties again. I am so lazy sometimes. I was unable to do all of my weaving three days in a row, and maman was so mad at me. I was not able to overcome my tiredness to complete those things I was entrusted with. Also, when maman beat me I felt a deep loss within me, Father, and I had terrible trouble knowing and trusting that God was there with me in my trial. I also had much difficulty praying for her. I struggled in finding enough love in my heart to forgive her."

"You did eventually forgive her, did you not?" inquired the priest.

"Yes, Father, I forgave her. She is so unhappy and I know she needs my prayers. But I struggled to let go of my hurt. I am so sorry. Also, I lacked joy, Father; I only showed my heart's sorrows yesterday. The children who came to me in the field saw sadness in me and not the Lord's joy and generosity. Oh Father, I truly lacked the faithfulness to the Lord's request to bear all things with patience. Truly, Father, I felt such darkness come over me."

Father Sabrières counseled her, "My child, God recognizes our weaknesses; He is aware of our wretched nature and to what degree we are indeed powerless in the face of darkness. You must know, my child, that God chooses those souls He has fashioned to submit perfectly to His will, so that He may reduce them, through humiliation and suffering, to such pitiful states that the world fails to see God's loving hand at work; it is unable to understand God's mysterious workings. But know this, child, that this pitiable state, unless achieved, a soul would be unable to resist the assaults of presumptuous pride. It is then that the soul, having lost hope in God's benevolence, begins to offend Him greatly by secretly trusting more in himself. Remember, child, the Lord our God permits no evil to afflict us that His power and His goodness have not already transformed into something good. You must guard against discouragement, my child, even though you may constantly fail to keep your repeated resolutions. From these shortcomings, my child, rather than relying on yourself to overcome this darkness that surrounds you, learn instead utter distrust in yourself, and rely completely on God. As a daily meditation, I would like you to repeat these words often:

"I shall do nothing, Lord, unless you cause me to do it. I will rely on your grace, my Lord, for it alone suffices."

"Yes, Father, I will repeat this faithfully," Germaine assured her confessor.

"Now say your act of contrition," Father Sabrières instructed.

Germaine began to recite the act of contrition she had memorized long ago during Sunday afternoon catechism classes: "O my Jesus, I am heartily sorry for all of my sins, and I detest them above all things for fear of the loss of my soul and especially for fear of the loss of your friendship, my Jesus, whom I love, because I know they displease thee, who are so infinitely good and lovable. I firmly resolve with the help of thy grace to do penance for them, and never more to offend thee."

Simultaneously, Father Sabrières prayed in Latin and gave her absolution in the vernacular: "Your sins are forgiven. You may now go in peace."

Back at the house, Armande, Laurent, and Pierre Dauvet the farmhand, were sitting at the table, eating a modest lunch. Suddenly, Pierre grabbed a small loaf of bread and stood up.

Armande inquired, "Where do you think you are going?"

The farmhand paused for a moment and then said, "It's my turn to bring Germaine her food."

Armande looked angry for a moment, but quickly regained her composure, and said, "That's right. Some of the scraps left over from the dog will do. Bring those to her instead." Armande reached out and grabbed the loaf from Pierre, handing him instead the dog's dish. Laurent stopped eating and watched.

"Of course, madame Cousin," the young farmhand responded and left the house.

"What was that all about?" inquired Laurent.

"Your child has been feeding other people with our food."

"It's her food, so let her do as she wants with it," he responded abruptly.

"Maybe you have not been paying attention, my husband, but we are not exactly wealthy. You are not providing adequately for this family; because of that, this family's social status is diminished, and I have had to endure humiliation," Armande explained. Laurent, resigned, looked down at his plate.

Pierre Dauvet entered the barn and looked at where Germaine slept, at the altar on which the wooden crucifix made of sticks rested, and the sheepskin she used to keep her warm. She was, of course, shepherding the herd at La Bouconne, so he placed her ration of dog food on a wooden stump for when she came back. He felt such sorrow as he looked at her living conditions.

The next morning in the downtown main street of Pibrac, Bernard sat with his back against a building. Germaine, returning from morning mass, approached him. "Are you hungry, Monsieur Bernard?"

Bernard looked up at Germaine and smiled. "Yes, but don't waste your food on me, Germaine."

Germaine sat next to him and said, "Nonsense. Giving you food is not a waste."

"Save some food for yourself, Germaine. It looks like you could use a meal more than I," counseled Bernard, who could see Germaine's emaciated body and facial features.

"I'll be fine," Germaine replied most joyfully. She continued, "There are others who need it more than me."

Bernard, touched by the girl's simplicity and joy, replied, "You know, you are too kind to me."

"There's no such thing as too kind, Monsieur Bernard," Germaine replied in a corrective tone.

"Here's what I think," Bernard exclaimed. "When you spend all your energy on others, you leave none for yourself. And if you don't pay attention to yourself, you end up like me." Bernard cautioned, "I don't want you to end up like me."

She replied with conviction, "Jesus is my shepherd, and so there is nothing I shall want. He will guide me and bring me to do the things He wants done. Then He will bring me home."

"O my dear Germaine, your trust is disarming," Bernard commented, his eyes welling up.

Germaine replied, "I must go now, monsieur. I need to attend to my sheep waiting in the field."

"I know, I know," replied Bernard. "You have much to do. But what are your sheep doing now, without a shepherd?"

"Oh! Jesus's angels are tending to them while I am away," responded Germaine nonchalantly.

"Just be safe while near the forest," Bernard cautioned. As Germaine stood up, Bernard looked at her and smiled. Germaine smiled back at him ever so gently with a nod of her head. Bernard quickly scrambled to his feet and bowed to her while removing his hat, saying, "Always nice to see you, Mademoiselle Cousin."

"Thank you, monsieur, for your kindness," Germaine replied as she departed.

The next day, Germaine, her face and eyes blackened with bruises and contusions from a previous day's beating, walked out near La Bouconne forest with her sheep. Now surrounded by more numerous children, her popularity having grown considerably since the parting of the waters, Germaine continued to speak of Jesus and the angels to those who cared to listen.

"Every little suffering or hurt is to be offered up to Jesus in a simple way," insisted Germaine. "It's not really complicated.

Just say to Jesus: please take this headache and use it as you will for the conversion of sinners." Germaine would joyfully instruct the children after they had played enough and were ready to settle down to listen to her.

"Do you mean I can give Jesus the cut on my finger for sinners?" asked a giggly girl.

"Oh! What about the bruise on my knee? Will Jesus take that also?" piped up a little boy, whose eyes twinkled with delight.

"He sure will. He'll take all your sufferings," assured Germaine. She continued her teaching on suffering with such joy that the children listened with great intent. "Now do no fear approaching the cross, for it will purify you, and as it does, it will give glory to God in heaven."

That night in the barn, as in so many nights before, Germaine would have to put into practice what she taught in words to the children. Having followed Germaine to the pasture several times over the previous week to see how she managed her time, Armande witnessed firsthand Germaine feeding bread to the poor. Knowing that the little portion of bread she gave Germaine as a daily ration was insufficient to feed a mouse let alone a 19 years-old girl, Armande reasoned that the bountiful bread portions she was handing out to the poor had to have been stolen. That night she was prepared to punish Germaine for her sin.

"I saw you in the field the other day, giving the household bread to the vagrant poor. I told you many times not give our bread to those filthy despicable vagrants and their children. Why you seem to give bread to all the poor children of the region.

What am I to do with you? From now on, I am cutting your daily portion of bread in half, now we shall see how generous you are with my bread?" Armande informed Germaine with a threatening tone.

Germaine, speechless as she faced her tormentor, attempted to defend herself: "Madame, I truly did not steal any bread from the home. I promise you. The bread was from all the daily portions I was unable to eat."

"Shut up, impudent wretch! How dare you talk back at me with that tone!" Armanda shouted back with rage as she quickly grabbed one of the brooms and hit Germaine repeatedly, causing her to collapse to the floor, where Armande looked down on her with disgust. After ten minutes of brutal strikes to Germaine's body, Armande threw the broom on the floor and walked out saying, "I will beat you to a pulp if your chores are not done by tomorrow morning. Have I made myself clear?" Germaine remained curled up in a ball for a moment before retching up her last piteous meal.

Suddenly an angel appeared, engulfing the barn in a bright mystical light and approached Germaine, who had been so terribly beaten that she could not even lift her head. The angelic presence comforted her and delicately tended to her wounds. After some time, the angel said, "Germaine! Rise up."

Germaine was suddenly able to look up and see the luminous being standing in front of her; she hesitated, and stood up slowly, healed from her multiple wounds; the pain that had previously overtook her had greatly diminished. Germaine's face and body were radiant with a beauty and splendor that transcended the worldly realm. She asked, "Who are you that you should come to me in my suffering and misery?"

The angel replied, "I am Raphael, and the Lord your God has sent me to comfort you, for the blows you did receive tonight would have killed you. Take heart and continue your journey to Jesus's cross. There, He, who is all glory in the heavens and on earth, awaits you." The angel faded and the barn was again plunged into darkness. Germaine then fell to her knees, her head bent down in humility.

Meanwhile, Armande, who had been tending the fire, looked out of the house window in the direction of the barn, and saw the surreal light vanish suddenly. She became troubled and perplexed by what she thought she had seen. Quickly, she dismissed any thoughts she may have had, saying, "This cannot be. The devil must be playing tricks on me," and continued to stoke the fire.

Weeks later, the first snow of the season had fallen, leaving a thin layer on the ground. The sun was hidden behind a dark gray sky. Germaine, in the barn, filled up her apron with pieces of bread she had been setting aside from her daily rations. She set out in the direction of the town, her apron filled with the pieces of bread she planned to give to the poor who lined the road to Pibrac, and to those scattered throughout the town; she did this on occasion on days when she planned to take the sheep out to pasture later in the morning. It tended to be on days when she needed to thoroughly clean out the barn. She held the apron close to her chest with her left hand. As she walked, she encountered a few travelers headed in the opposite direction. As they approached her, the travelers, after catching sight of the terrible sores on her neck and the bruises on her face which she had sustained from her frequent beatings, would turn away from her. Behind Germaine, about two kilometers back, was Armande, following her into town with the intent of catching her in the act of stealing. She was determined to show the entire town, once and for all, that Germaine was a deceiver and a thief. She had finally seen her filling her dress apron with bread that she suspected had been taken from the house. *Now I will be vindicated*, Armande thought.

The main street was quiet on that cold and cloudy late November day. One woman walked by hurriedly, carrying a basket of herbs she had purchased in the town market. The town square was full of vendors with broken-down carts loaded with wool, fish, bread, and various other commodities appropriate for the season. This is Pibrac in the 1590s. It is a town full of struggling farmers. There are beggars, hungry children, men and women of all ages trying to simply get by.

Germaine finally looked behind her and saw Armande, about a kilometer away, increase her step in order to catch up to her. In response, Germaine began walking with greater urgency. Sensing the stepmother approaching, and overcome with great fear that she would be beaten, Germaine began running in the direction of the town square. Armande suddenly yelled out, "Someone stop her. Stop the thief!"

The townspeople took notice of the clamor and began to gather around. Germaine turned and looked with surprise at Armande running in her direction; she could not understand why her stepmother was accusing her of theft. The young maiden came to a stop as she entered the square, embarrassed and overwhelmed with fatigue. She looked all around her and saw the townspeople staring at her as they hemmed her in, preventing her from running any farther.

Armande finally managed to catch up to her and, grabbing her left arm, yelled out for everyone to hear, "I've caught you in the act this time, Germaine. I saw you from outside the barn putting my bread into your apron to feed those pathetic peasants. Now everyone will know what I suspected for a long time; that you are a filthy thief. What you hold in your apron, Germaine, is what will condemn you," the overbearing matriarch cried out.

Armande tried to force Germaine's apron open, but Germaine leaned backward, moving out of Armande's strong grasp. As Armande let go of Germaine's arm she slapped her hard on the face, leaving Germaine stunned for a moment. Then Armande shouted, "Give back the bread now!"

Armande slowly walked in the direction of Germaine, reveling in the knowledge that she was going to finally expose Germaine and show everyone that she was nothing more than a thief.

"Do you see this child?" asked Armande, a contrived sense of righteousness written all over her face. "Do you see the wretched burden I bear day after day? She has once again stolen bread from our pantry. It is hidden in her apron! Look how she conceals her deception. Of course she denies it, because she is also a liar!"

Germaine looked down at Armande's feet, fearing for her stepmother's soul, concerned for the hatred and the falsehood she was now exhibiting. Looking up into Armande's eyes, Germaine pleaded with a soft whisper so as not to be heard by the townspeople, "Please, madame, this is from the rations you give me, and the children to whom I bring this bread need it more than I."

"Listen to her, she lies right to my face! And then admits to stealing," Armande protested. "Look at her, God has afflicted her with lameness. He has even cursed the girl's face so as to warn us of the evil inside her! Surely He would not do this to a pure soul! Now would He?" Armande inquired, her voice strained with loathing. Germaine noticed the growing crowd gathered all around her and Armande, their eyes fixated on her. She tensed up with embarrassment.

"Please, madame. The children are hungry; don't prevent me from helping them," Germaine begged again in a whisper.

The strict and stringent matriarch was unaffected by the supplication; she remained unmoved by her request. Turning to the crowd, the stepmother commanded, "Show them, Germaine; show them what you have stolen from me!"

Armande reached for Germaine's apron and pulled the apron strings from her hands, causing its content to fall to the ground. But instead of the expected scraps of bread falling, an array of beautiful and colorful flowers floated out of Germaine's apron and slowly fell to the street. The townspeople were astonished by this miracle. There were many hushed exclamations heard amidst the large crowd.

Armande, taken aback by this turn of events, turned and ran out of the town square in embarrassment. The townspeople slowly approached Germaine, who was still staring at the flowers spread across the ground.

Joseph Champin, the town's baker, exclaimed, "They are beautiful. I have never seen such flowers in this area. How can this be?"

Andre Le Voyeur then interjected, "Especially in winter." Germaine, instead of being overjoyed at this, looked crestfallen, saddened by Armande's continued hardness of heart.

Germaine turned to the townspeople and said, "They are beautiful, but now I have nothing with which to feed the hungry."

Joseph Champin walked into the circle, carrying several loaves of bread, which he gave to Germaine, saying, "Here, take these loaves in order to feed them. You are truly good and pure. God bless you, Germaine." Joseph tried to contain his emotions, but he could not stop his eyes from welling up with tears.

Germaine looked at the bread and then, beholding the baker with eyes of unbelievable purity and joy, said, "God bless you, sir," as she took the bread loaves and placed them in her apron.

10

The Priests Begin to Change
Their Stance

*"But the foolish things of the world hath God chosen, that
he may confound the wise: and the weak things of the
world hath God chosen, that he may confound the strong."*

—1 Corinthians 1:27 (Douay-Rheims Bible)

In the rectory the next day, Father Sabrières and the two
assistant priests were sitting around a long table in the
rectory's meeting room. They had been discussing the rumors
they were hearing about Germaine Cousin. Silence had settled
for a moment in the room, as each of the priests began to
contemplate the mysterious nature of these events. Finally,
Father Guillaume Carrière broke the silence. "It seems you were

216

correct, Father Sabrières. There is something special about that peasant girl after all!"

"I take no pride in being right. I was simply given a grace to see with great clarity in this case," Father Jean explained quite humbly.

The second assistant priest, Jehan Hoguet, who had remained silent for most of the discussion, finally added, "Well, with so many people coming forward with miraculous stories about Germaine, we must take some action, I would think."

Father Carrière quickly replied, "I agree. But what shall we do?"

"I honestly do not know," responded Father Hoguet. "But one thing is certain: we should not ignore these…well… miracles. Plus, I have been seeing significant numbers of repentant sinners coming in droves to confession because of her. I don't know what to make of this."

Father Sabrières promptly cut in, "Father Hoguet, we mustn't move too quickly in pronouncing them as 'miracles.' Only the Church can rule with authority in these matters." He remained pensive and pondered very carefully the words he was going to speak, and then continued, "And so we must wait and be very cautious. I do not want a word spoken about the phenomena witnessed around the Cousin girl by any of the clergy. We are to proceed as if nothing has happened."

"But what do we do when parishioners approach us and ask us questions?" Father Guillaume inquired.

"Answer nothing; change the subject, advise them to no longer speak of this matter," Father Sabrières responded with decisiveness. "The last thing that we want is to make Germaine into a spectacle. She needs our protection, and we need to shield her from the world's corruption. Now that the Lord's favors clearly surround her, we must protect her from the ever-growing risk of pride. She may indeed be a pure child precious to the Lord Jesus. Our goal is to keep her that way. God have mercy on us, should we, in any way, corrupt this young maiden by not shielding her from fame or by edifying her by flattery."

"What should we do to protect her, then?" Father Jehan Hoguet inquired with eager interest. Turning to Father Sabrières, he added, "I could personally speak to Laurent Cousin, if you wish."

"Laurent is a weak man, and has protected her very little over the years. What would you expect to accomplish by talking with him?" asked Father Sabrières.

Father Guillaume piped up, "I think that is entirely appropriate. Jehan could possibly persuade him of his obligations as a father to protect her. In any event, the girl needs our assistance, this is certain."

Father Jehan continued, "Should we be offering her an opportunity to discern whether or not to enter the Jacobin convent in Toulouse? We may be looking at a vocation here?"

Father Sabrières, warming his hands over the fire, his back turned in the direction of his assistant priest, replied, his voice deep and meditative, "I have thought about this already, but I believe we need to discern more about these phenomena surrounding Germaine. I am not sure what to make of them. I have never heard of these kinds of miraculous events occurring to a young girl like that before. Well, not since Catherine of Siena anyway; that was close to two hundred years ago. We must tread carefully, so as not to scandalize the faithful. I will nevertheless approach her and her father about a vocational discernment."

Father Hoguet, wanting to be supportive, responded, "I tend to agree that we should approach the subject carefully, but we mustn't forget that the young maiden is ill with scrofula and has a lame right hand and arm. She would have difficulties completing the physical duties that would be demanded of her in a convent."

"That is an excellent point. I will keep that in mind when I approach them both," replied Father Jean.

11

Big Changes at the Cousin Home

The Lord turns his eyes to the just and his ears to their appeal. They call and the Lord hears and rescues them in all their distress.

—Psalter based on Psalm 34:12–15, 17–18

Father Jean-Granet Sabrières was sitting behind the desk in the rectory office, his fingers piously folded over one another, his eyes locked on Laurent Cousin. "Laurent, I do not know what to make of all these stories about Germaine. The miraculous flowers that fell from her apron, yesterday, have made of Germaine a sensation in the eyes of the world."

Laurent replied, his voice hesitant and awkward, unable to contain the sense of helplessness that he felt. "I don't understand anything, Father. I wasn't there when it happened, but I have been hearing stories from almost everyone, since yesterday. I don't know what to think anymore, either."

"Laurent, listen to me very carefully," Father Sabrières spoke up, determined to embolden him to protect his daughter more. "Your daughter may be the recipient of divine graces, the likes of which we may never see again in our lifetime. You have a responsibility as her father to protect her and to see to it that she is not troubled by these events. And so you must shield her from onlookers and troublesome sorts that may seek to harm her."

That evening at the table, Laurent and Armande were talking while casually consuming their meal. Laurent was trying to persuade Armande to lighten Germaine's workload. Finally, frustrated by her unwillingness to be more flexible, Laurent stood up and slammed his hands on the table, startling Armande, who was silenced by his resolute determination. Armande had never seen this kind of authority and strength in Laurent before.

"Armande!" Laurent said loudly before clearing his throat. "This abuse of Germaine will come to an end this evening. As God is my witness, you will never lay a hand on her again. I am going to invite her back into the home to be among us. She is my daughter, and I will protect her. If I should hear of any abuses again, God have mercy on your soul and on mine!" He walked out of the house, slamming the door behind him.

With a determined walk, he headed over to the barn, but as he approached, his pace relented. He was so ashamed of his weakness and inability to defend Germaine from Armande's assaults. He felt his guilt and shame weigh heavily upon him.

Laurent opened the barn door with trepidation, and hesitantly looked around. He had never gone into the barn since Armande had banished Germaine there, sixteen years earlier. He shivered slightly, disgusted by the miserable conditions in which Germaine had been living. Laurent stood at the doorway of the barn, his eyes immersed in misery. He looked at Germaine lying down in her bed, his eyes horrified. He could not speak; he was overcome by emotion, paralyzed by shame and guilt. He walked to her bedside and knelt beside her as she slept. He stroked her brow gently just as a father should; his eyes were filled with compassion.

Gently, Laurent whispered into Germaine's ear, "Germaine! Germaine!"

Germaine eyes opened suddenly. As she sat up, she said, "Oui, papa!"

A long moment of silence overtook Laurent as he looked at her, unable to speak.

All of sudden, Laurent, incapable of thinking of anything he could say that would wipe away the serious consequences of his weakness as a man and father, said, "Do you need another blanket, my dear?"

"No, thank you, papa!" Germaine replied with total and complete simplicity. There was no guile in her.

Laurent continued, "Listen, I am so very sorry about abandoning you, and for not defending you."

"Don't be sorry for anything, papa. It's all right," replied Germaine with great gentleness.

Laurent let out a long sigh, before replying, "No, Germaine, it's not all right. I let Armande make my decisions for me, and I turned my back on you." Laurent sat down before continuing. "I thought…It doesn't matter what I thought. It seems like every step I've taken has been the wrong one. My heart was cold toward you, Germaine. I didn't care, and I didn't want to know. And now, I realize—Ah! I am so ashamed of myself. I have sinned against God, against you, and against charity."

"Speak no more, papa! It isn't necessary," supplicated Germaine, pained by her father's suffering.

Laurent persisted, he could not be quiet, he continued with his confession. "I was weak and did not care! I only thought about myself. What I did was wrong; I have sinned against heaven and earth." Laurent stood up and looked down on Germaine sitting up on her bed of straw.

"I want you to move into the house. There is plenty of room; I need you to return," lamented Laurent.

Germaine looked up at him and said, "Non, papa. Thank you, but I prefer it here. I've come to know Jesus here, in this solitude. O! How I would mourn if I were to lose Him by embracing the comforts of the world."

"But, Germaine," protested Laurent. "This is for your own good."

"Non, papa, I must stay here for it is better for my soul." As Germaine coughed into her right hand, she saw blood in her palm, and immediately hid it from her father.

"Are you certain, my child?" Laurent persisted.

"Oui, papa! It is better," replied Germaine.

Laurent, feeling that he was getting nowhere, finally said, "Well, I have to get back to the house, but the door remains opened to you, always, Germaine. Forgive me, my daughter."

"Please, papa, you are forgiven, I never faulted you," Germaine assured her papa.

With fatherly eyes that seemed to have grown in wisdom, Laurent looked at her for a moment, and then left.

"Papa?" Germaine called aloud.

Laurent stopped and turned towards her. "Yes?"

"I love you very much. I always have," replied Germaine.

Laurent, his face pained by his failure as a man, replied, "Bless you, Germaine," and left.

At the church, Germaine and Father Sabrières sat alone in the pew, in the very spot long ago where he'd informed her that her mother had died. They spoke so softly that their conversation echoed as a murmur in the silence. Germaine looked sad.

"Germaine, you might like to think about entering the Jacobin convent in Toulouse. It would be a much better life for you compared to what you have here. Have you ever thought of a religious vocation?" asked Father Sabrières.

"Oh, Father, I am not familiar with this convent. In any event, I have never wished for this. Truly, I am undeserving of such an honor. You know that I cannot even read or write," explained Germaine.

"They will teach you these things, Germaine. The sisters are very good in that way," Father Sabrières reassured Germaine, who was visibly uncomfortable about being offered such a high position. *Her humility is baffling*, thought Father Sabrières.

"Oh, Father, I am so stupid. I don't know that I could even learn to read or write," Germaine admitted most earnestly. She continued after a brief pause. "But if the Lord wills it for me, I should be so happy to enter the convent," she conceded, as she began to get up to return home.

"Germaine, I ask only that you pray about this. Ask Jesus to assist you in discerning His most holy will," Father Sabrières carefully instructed.

"I will, Father," Germaine replied as she left the church.

The next day, Germaine and Bernard were sitting out in the pasture near La Bouconne forest, watching the sheep. Germaine looked pale. She coughed into a handkerchief. Bernard looked at her with sadness in his eyes.

"My poor Germaine, you don't look so good today," pointed out Bernard, concerned.

"I'm tired, Bernard, very tired," Germaine replied with a sigh.

"I tell you, Germaine, you need to rest."

"O Bernard, I rest too much already. There is so little time," Germaine explained.

"What do you mean, Germaine, so little time? There's lots of time, my dear. You are still so young," exclaimed Bernard, who was feeling uneasy. "God visibly favors you; the miracles that have occurred around you, Germaine, are a clear sign of His love for you. Pray for me that Jesus might have mercy on my poor soul," Bernard requested with heartfelt concern for his sad state.

"Bernard, you are always in my prayers," Germaine assured him.

Bernard suddenly turned toward Germaine, got down on his two knees, and, bowing his head, said, "Bless me, Germaine."

Germaine kissed Bernard on the forehead and said with the most delicate and pure voice, "I cannot bless you, Bernard; a priest's blessing is far greater than mine. Return to the church, Bernard, and the Lord will shower you with blessings and graces."

"I will return, Germaine. I am such a poor, miserable sinner."

Germaine struggled to her feet. "I must return to my sheep. Pray for me, Bernard," asked Germaine, who was unusually more introspective.

"Germaine, from the bottom of my heart, I will pray for you," assured Bernard.

12

Mystical Lights from Heaven

As gold in the furnace, he proved them, and as sacrificial offerings he took them to himself.

—Canticle, Book of Wisdom: 3:1–6

That night, Germaine was lying on her bed of straw, covered up by three thick blankets, but still shivering. She looked very pale and weak. Celestial light, perhaps it was moonlight, poked through one of the holes in the ceiling and immersed her in a beam that appeared to warm and comfort her; it was the summer of 1601.

Suddenly, Armande burst into the barn, the light having faded moments before Armande could see it.

"You insolent little tramp," Armande yelled. "I know what you are trying to do. You will not succeed in turning everyone against me."

Germaine, too weak to argue, made no effort to protest.

"Your innocent demeanor will have no effect on me. I have put up with you for a long time. Now, it has become intolerable," thundered Armande.

"I have never meant to be difficult. I am so sorry that I caused you grief. Please forgive me," pleaded Germaine.

"Forgive you?" said Armande. "I don't believe there will be any forgiveness for you, my dear," seethed Armande, whose hatred for Germaine had reached new heights. She continued to berate her, saying, "I will never forgive you for what you have done to me and to my children. Their untimely deaths are your fault. My life has been sheer misery because of you. I cannot stand you; you repulse me, Germaine! I will see to it that everyone, including your father, sees right through your falsehood, and all of the staged antics you have been fabricating. You are such a miserable deceiver. I pray that God have mercy on your poor soul," Armande cried out as she left the barn in haste.

Germaine whispered softly, almost imperceptibly, "I forgive you."

A prayer heard by nobody but the Lord Himself, who stood close by to receive it.

Upon exiting, Armande leaned back against the wall of the barn and began to cry. Inside, hidden from Armande, a light showered Germaine in a brightness that was not of this world, while angels surrounded her and began clothing her mystical

body with a white wedding garment—symbol of her virginity—
for the great banquet that awaited her.

Her guardian angel said to her," It is time to prepare my
little one."

Two catholic monks, traveling from Gascony to the
city of Toulouse, lost their way in the vicinity of Pibrac as
nightfall blanketed the region in darkness. As they were
preparing to settle down to sleep in the nearby field, a
beautiful light pierced through the darkened sky and bathed
a little barn, far off in the distance, in a shimmering
glow. The mystical light drew them, beckoning them to
come nearer. As the two monks slowly approached, they
hid behind a tree just in time to witness celestial beings
that looked like angels descending into the barn, and
another group walking through the forest in the direction of
the barn. Then they observed a beautiful maiden
accompanying these angels back through the forest on their
way to heaven. They got a good look at the young woman
who was wearing a crown of flowers on her head, a veil,
and a white wedding robe. Her face radiated with a
heavenly beauty, they concluded, could most certainly
not be of this world. Their hearts were filled with joy from
this encounter.

"I've never even dreamed of such beauty," the first
monk said, his eyes wide open in awe.

"Nor have I," replied Brother Jamet, dumbfounded by
the vision.

"The maiden was a virgin," Brother Clement concluded,
for she wore the veil and the wedding dress that is donned as

a symbol by the brides of Christ. "What a sight to behold!" he proclaimed.

They devoutly knelt on the very ground they stood on, and began to pray, giving praise for God's glory.

"We must get closer to see this wonder," exclaimed Brother Clement, who could still see the barn illuminated.

"Oh no! We mustn't get nearer; we should not approach, for that is surely holy ground," cautioned Brother Jamet.

The two men remained motionless, looking at the splendor of God's angels assisting that beautiful virgin as they rose in unison to heaven.

"I wonder who the maiden is that the Lord would surround her with such beauty and glory?" said Brother Clement.

"I know not, brother, but her beauty was of such purity that I am almost speechless," said Brother Jamet.

As they continued to gaze at that wondrous spectacle, the light and the angels gradually faded into the night.

"We must still be another fifteen minutes from Pibrac," brother Clement said. "Perhaps we should hurry and inform the pastor at the local church what we saw. My Lord and my God, what wonders you have shown us!"

"Of course, you are right! Let's walk in haste," said Brother Jamet. The two religious eventually came scampering up the road in the direction of St. Mary Magdalene Church in Pibrac. When they got to the door, Brother Clement knocked impatiently.

Father Sabrières was reciting the divine office in his bedroom when he heard the insistent knocks. He got up to answer the door. When he opened it, he saw the two religious standing before him, traits of humility and prayerfulness drawn upon their faces.

"May peace be with you, dear brothers. How may I be of assistance to you at this late hour?" inquired the pastor.

"We beg your pardon for intruding, Father, but we've witnessed something quite remarkable. So incredible, in fact that, both Brother Clement and I believed it urgent to contact you at once," explained the outspoken monk.

"You're not intruding. I am Father Sabrières, the pastor here, so please enter and let me serve you something to refresh you. These summer evenings can be uncomfortably warm and humid. Madame Laguère," the pastor shouted. "Could you be so kind as to offer our guests some beverages?" Father Sabrières patiently requested.

"Ah! Oui, mon père, tout de suite," the housemaid replied as she entered the room. Having heard the thumping on the door, Alesta Laguère promptly awoke and rose swiftly from her bed, ready to be of service to the pastor. Over the years, it was not an uncommon occurrence for late evening guests to meet with Father Sabrières in the rectory. This old widow had become used to serving parishioners, who consulted the priests for spiritual guidance, barley tea and bread; the menu almost never varied. Tonight, however, because she found the monks rather emaciated, Alesta preferred to serve them something more substantive. Three hardy slices of cheese served with bread, complemented with a brandy, is what she finally concocted.

"Now, my dear friends in Christ, what have you seen?" asked Father Sabrières, a smile on his lips, certain they were about to recount some wild ghost story; he had heard so many over the years, that he no longer took these accounts seriously. He had decided that he would politely listen to them, and then bring the meeting hastily to a close so that he could get back to reciting his office.

Brother Jamet cleared his throat, paused for a moment in order to gain his composure, and then began to recount the event. "Father, we were traveling to Toulouse from Gascony, but lost our way just outside of Pibrac; it got so dark. So we were getting ready to settle down for the night in the field along Chemin des Bourdettes, perhaps 1.5 miles from Pibrac. It was at that moment that we saw the most wondrous thing."

"Yes, Father," interjected Brother Clement, "it was incredible; it was beautiful! And that's when it happened."

"What happened?" inquired Father Sabrières, suddenly showing a little more interest.

Brother Clement continued, "We saw from a distance a very bright light shine down from heaven, and in the light there appeared to be several beautiful angels coming down to earth. And then, as we stood there, rapt by the heavenly vision, we observed, walking through the woods, a group of heavenly maidens unencumbered by their physical surroundings, singing the most beautiful songs that filled the forest with splendor. They came within thirty feet of us, unaffected by our presence, floating effortlessly in the air. I tell you assuredly that their feet were not touching the earth. Upon seeing this—"

Brother Jamet quickly interrupted. "We immediately fell to our knees and began to pray. And then, a short time later, a choir of angels interspersed with the same maidens passed again, but this time their radiance and joy was magnified as they were now accompanied by another, a most beautiful maiden wearing a crown of flowers and a white wedding robe. Her skin was most radiant and she walked by us like a princess surrounded by her ladies-in-waiting. It was most beautiful. Then they vanished… just like that. Brother Clement and I had never seen anything like it before."

Father Sabrières was collected, his eyes fixed on his guests, the features of his face as if frozen in time. "You were on route to Toulouse from Gascony, you say?" The priest inquired. "Was there a farm in the vicinity of this vision?"

"Yes, there was. In fact, the lights shone on one specific farm that was nearby," Brother Clement eagerly answered.

Father Sabrières continued with his inquiry. "Was the farmhouse maybe situated right along the road? There is a small sheep farm that is nestled not far from Chemin des Bourdettes," he explained.

"That is most certainly the place," answered Brother Clement enthusiastically. "Whose farm does it belong to, Father?"

"My God," the pastor exclaimed. "It is Laurent Cousin's farm. It is where Germaine lives; she comes to my church." Jean-Granet Sabrières's throat tightened up, and his facial expression became somber.

13

A Light Has Been Extinguished

"Let all bitterness and anger and indignation and clamour and blasphemy be put away from you, with all malice."

—Ephesians 4:31–32 (Douay-Rheims Bible)

Armande was preparing Germaine's body for burial. She dressed her in the finest dress she could find. Her face, hardened by time and age, showed very little expression as she brushed Germaine's hair. Suddenly she broke down. "Dear God, forgive me for what I did to this child. I was wrong. I beg your forgiveness, Germaine. I see now, how sick with pride and anger I have become. May God have mercy on me for all I did to you," she cried out and then wept for a good long while as she finished Germaine's wardrobe preparations.

Almost the entire town walked along with the procession that carried Germaine into the church for the funeral mass. Because many suspected her holiness, it had been decided by Father Sabrières that she should be interred under the flagstone floor in front of the pulpit.

The parishioners filled the pews, reverently bowing their heads before the altar as they quietly sat down. They pondered the life of this victim soul who had walked among them. She had been of no stately appearance or importance; she had been despised, much like our Lord. Many of the parishioners stood at the back as there were no more seats available. The pallbearers walked Germaine's casket up to the front, near the sanctuary. Many had come to attend the funeral from all over les Midi-Pyrénées and the Haute-Garonne, in particular.

Father Sabrières processed up to the high altar with the two other priests, Fathers Carrière and Hoguet, and three altar boys; the one leading the procession held the cross high above his head. The choir chanted the "Miserere Mei" in Latin. It was a solemn mass, and all those present pondered the marvels surrounding Germaine's life. Many felt a deep remorse for the neglect and the ridicule they all had directed at her. So many souls sobbed that day! Following the gospel reading, Father Sabrières somberly walked to the ambo to give his homily.

He looked at the congregation with sharp and saddened eyes. He began to speak, "My brothers and sisters in Christ, the spirit of wisdom is lacking in our day. And yet beyond all else, Scripture tells us that we should prefer wisdom. Why is that? Because the wise person knows what he aspires to…what he thirsts for, since wisdom enables him to truly see what most cannot. In the gospel of Mark, the rich man lacks this wisdom. First, because, as he stands before Jesus, he is unaware of the one who stands before him. Indeed, he comes before Jesus unable to comprehend the deepest need and longing of his heart, for he is a prisoner of his crippling self-reliance. Have we not also become like him, afflicted by a pride that so cripples our souls that we cannot see that Jesus invites us to exchange this belief in our own strength and self-reliance for a total dependence on Him? The rich man, the gospel tells us, went away sad because he could not abandon himself to Jesus; he could not throw himself in the arms of our Lord. We have been blind also, as many of us could not see that Christ was in our midst. Germaine Cousin did learn to rely completely on God's mercy; she had to, for there was little mercy given to her by her family or community. And yet despite our shortcomings, He filled her with His graces. He shrouded her life in wonders, yet also allowed suffering to afflict her. My brothers and sisters in Christ, Germaine's life reminds us that human suffering has a redemptive nature. Let us pray for her soul, and let us practice penance in reparation for our sins and those of the whole world." The congregation quietly left the church with a somber mood. Armande, Laurent, Bernard, and the two monks, Clement and Jamet, walked quietly among the crowd that had gathered to witness this holy maiden's last requiem. Something happened in Pibrac that cannot be explained. Human nature does not easily embrace wonder, for most have lost the childlike awe needed to witness those supernatural events that God permits the innocent and the pure to see. Sometimes, He lets those unworthy of such marvels to see His glory; why He allows this, few can explain, for although most souls thirst for them, these glimpses into eternity, it would seem, are most often never permitted for those whose hearts have grown hard and cold.

14

Dealing with the Incorrupt Body

Because the eyes of the Lord are upon the just, and his ears unto their prayers but the countenance of the Lord upon them that do evil things."

—1 Peter 3:12 (Douay-Rheims Bible)

After discovering Germaine's body, Father Sounilhac took very little time before placing her remains in full exposition in front of the church ambo, and in very close proximity to Marie de Clement Gras's reserved pew. Her husband, François de Beauregard, was a prominent businessman in Pibrac, and a generous benefactor of the Catholic Church. They were considered among the nobility of Pibrac because of their many generous gifts to the Church, and to the local orphanage. Madame de Beauregard was involved in so many different altruistic endeavors within Pibrac society that it was hard to keep track of her. She was pious, charitable, and benevolent; she was a woman who, without a doubt, exemplified excellence in taste, social graces, and humor. If there was any kind of good and charitable effort being promoted in Pibrac society, Madame de Beauregard was always either an organizer or promoter of the cause.

The exposition of Germaine Cousin's corpse close to the ambo in Mary Magdalene's church was, however, very unsettling to Madame de Beauregard, who greatly appreciated order, cleanliness, and reason. Having a corpse right beside her pew appeared to her as one of those unreasonable things that she could not easily comprehend or stomach. It was the twelfth Sunday in a row that Madame de Beauregard had to sit next to Germaine's incorrupt corpse, and she was at the point of complete disgust. Taking her normal pious stance, rosary beads in hand, her head bowed low, she recited the rosary at an unusually fast pace. Her eyes nervously shifted between the casket and the Virgin's statue, unable to keep her mind on Mary, the subject of her veneration. Marie de Beauregard looked at her husband, her eyes wide opened and fierce, searching for some kind of sympathy for the agitation she was experiencing, but nothing from her husband's demeanor visibly supported her disgust. She patiently waited until mass had ended, before she cornered Father Sounilhac as he was walking from the sanctuary after removing his vestments in the sacristy.

It was while the priest was prayerfully pacing by her pew, his eyes clearly focused on the breviary he had in hand, that Marie de Beauregard quickly got up from her knees and stood directly in front of the priest, stopping him in his tracks. Looking at him directly, she said with an indignant tone, "Father Sounilhac, could I have a word with you?"

"Madame de Beauregard!" he said with some surprise, as he looked up from his missal. "How can I be of assistance?" the priest replied with genuine interest.

With her air evermore indignant, and her posture confrontational and ready for battle, she said, "Mon père, I would like to speak to you about the Cousin girl's corpse, and its proximity to our pew. It is very unsettling to my husband and I, and we wish that it be taken out of the church."

The priest replied, somewhat dismayed by Marie de Beauregard's request, "Madame de Beauregard, this is not possible, since hundreds of parishioners from St. Mary Magdalene's church, and from other churches around the diocese, and even from beyond, have been venerating her for months now. Why, it is miraculously causing cures, as well as miracles of conversion."

Marie de Beauregard pompously laughed aloud as she looked at the priest with righteous anger, saying, "Père Sounilhac, my husband and will not tithe to the parish anymore, unless you remove this disgusting corpse from the church. And need I remind you that our financial contributions have been quite substantive."

Father Sounilhac, his mouth open in disbelief, looked at Madame de Beauregard, astonished at her remarks. Then, having regained some composure, turned in the direction of François de Beauregard, as if to confirm the accuracy of his wife's threat. But to no avail did he perceive the needed confirmation. François, his head bowed low, did not dare look up, as he was ashamed of his wife's pretentiousness. Turning back to Marie de Beauregard, Father Sounilhac counseled, "Madame, you mustn't say such a thing about a possible saint. This kind of language could offend God most severely; His saints are rich gifts to the Church and should not be despised," Father Sounilhac responded with authority, and some trepidation in his voice, for holy fear had seized his heart.

"Father Sounilhac, my husband and I insist; we will immediately cancel the donation promised for the renovation of the sanctuary, unless you dispose of this grotesque cadaver immediately. Bury it or sell it, but if I see it again, the money you need will not be forthcoming. Have I made myself clear?" Marie de Beauregard angrily articulated, with not one single inflection indicating she was in the mood to negotiate anything with the priest.

Father Sounilhac, his eyes staring down at the floor, could not look at her. Over the last year, water had been leaking on to the altar and tabernacle when heavy rains had doused the region; her very generous donation made it possible to schedule the repairs earlier than predicted, just before the fall rains. He was at an impasse. He knew that he could do nothing other than to acquiesce to her demands, since the roof over the sanctuary was in serious need of repair. He responded with a voice barely perceptible, "Your donations have been very generous indeed." He paused, as if to collect his thoughts, and then continued, "I hear and acknowledge your request, and I will comply, madame." The fear he felt went deep; it was a spiritual fear for Madame de Beauregard's soul. He knew the seriousness of irreverently treating a holy relic, and feared for Madame de Beauregard's well-being after her display of disgust for Germaine Cousin's remains.

The next morning, immediately after mass, Father Sounilhac, along with his vicar, removed the shepherdess's casket and placed it in the sacristy, hidden from public view. As usual, hundreds of faithful were looking for their saint for veneration after mass, but nowhere could she be found. Rumors began circulating that either the anticlerical forces or the Huguenots had stolen her remains in the depth of night, in hopes of squashing the sudden rise in religious fervor that had taken place since her body had been exposed. Many were converting from Calvinism or atheism back to the Catholic Church because of this poor shepherdess.

Meanwhile, at the de Beauregard residence, Marie had collapsed, feverish and delirious, after finishing her breakfast. The doctor was called to assess her condition. She had developed infectious abscesses in both breasts, and could no longer breastfeed her new-born baby. Both were doing poorly at the time of the physician's visit.

"Madame de Beauregard needs rest and fluids," insisted Dr. Montant. "In addition, the baby's condition has also worsened. We must follow them both closely, as this can quickly turn very badly," he added as he stared at François de Beauregard, who was anxiously clutching his hands. "There is a surgeon in Toulouse whom I will contact promptly in order to get his opinion. I must act in haste before it is too late for both of them."

By the third day, the infection in both breasts had worsened and Marie's fever had increased along with the chills. The surgeon from Toulouse, Dr. Moreau, could not find a way to contain the spread of the infection. François de Beauregard, concerned with both his wife's and baby's health, promptly left the doctor and servant tending to his family and ran to church. There, kneeling at the altar railing, looking up at the tabernacle, François begged Jesus's forgiveness for his wife's disparaging remarks about His saint. He recognized as well his fault for not preventing his wife from confronting and threatening the pastor.

"My Lord and my God, I beseech you to forgive me for being such a weak husband, and I beg forgiveness, on behalf of my wife, for her disparaging words regarding your holy shepherdess Germaine Cousin. I commit to doing reparation for her sins and mine, but I beg you, in return, to spare the lives of my wife and child." He bowed his head, and then, resting his arms and head on the altar railing, began to weep.

At the house, the physician had applied the poultices to the breasts in order to draw out the infection. He gave the maid instructions to keep Marie de Beauregard comfortable until he returned in the morning to drain the breasts' abscesses: "Madame de Grand Maison, apply a new poultice before you retire for the night, and I will return in the morning to assess the situation. From what I can see, the infection is spreading; I am very worried. If things change for the worse during the night, tell Monsieur de Beauregard to come and get me."

"I will do as you say, Dr. Montant," replied Madame de Grand Maison with alarm in her voice, as she feared the worst. After the doctor left the house, the maid went directly to the kitchen to begin preparing Monsieur de Beauregard's evening meal.

In the bedroom, as Marie de Beauregard rested, a bright light flooded the room with such intensity that it stirred her out of her slumber. She looked at the light with astonishment, unable to see anything at first, except for a vague human form immersed in light, slowly approaching the bed; fright suddenly took hold of her as she was able to identify the entity as a young maiden resembling a shepherdess kneeling by her bed. Marie, terrified and incredulous all at the same time, called out, "Who are you?"

The shepherdess, her face beautifully transfigured with a loving smile, peacefully responded, "Do not be afraid. I am the shepherdess, Germaine Cousin, whom you persecute."

Marie de Beauregard, her mouth opened in disbelief, began to wail uncontrollably at first, but after a moment of frenetic weeping, called out to heaven, "My God, I have sinned against you and against one of your holy saints. I am a vile creature deserving hell, please forgive me, I implore you, Jesus."

Germaine replied, "This night, your husband François pleaded with our Lord before the tabernacle in the church, for your healing and that of your baby. The Lord was pleased with your husband's heartfelt supplication, and his commitment to do penance on your behalf; and Jesus will hold him to his promise. Because of your husband's love and his unrelenting appeal to the Lord's mercy, Jesus has consented to heal you and your baby."

Germaine then extended her hand, shimmering in light, over Marie's chest, then, slowly retrieving it, she faded away in the light.

As she sat up, Marie de Beauregard exclaimed with a loud voice that could be heard throughout the house, "I am healed! I am healed! Praise the Lord in heaven! Praise His angels and saints forever! François, Madame de Grand Maison, I am healed! I am healed!"

The next day, Madame de Beauregard was already up and around, busy with the baby, but decidedly determined to make amends with Father Sounilhac and God for her terrible comments about Germaine Cousin, and her shameful manipulation of the priest. Following a heartfelt confession at the church, she promptly made an appointment with Father Sounilhac in order to make arrangements to donate a beautiful lead casket to contain the incorrupt remains of the shepherdess she had so vehemently despised. Germaine's body was eventually transferred to the lead casket, which remained in the sacristy. However, to the surprise of everyone, Father Sounilhac ordered it sealed, fearing that a continued exposition of the incorrupt body to public view would incite excessive curiosity rather than true veneration. His experience with Madame de Beauregard taught him well to fear the derogatory comments and actions that could potentially come from the general public and even the parishioners.

Several months had elapsed, and still Father Sounilhac had not heard back from the Bishop of Toulouse, despite submitting his report, about the Cousin girl, a few weeks after discovering her incorrupt remains. The parishioners of St. Mary Magdalene Church were by now growing impatient about Germaine Cousin's cause. Was the bishop going to support her beatification and canonization? Will her incorrupt corpse ever be put on display again for all to venerate? In fact, all of Pibrac was talking about this long-forgotten saint whom the Lord now, it would seem, wished to make known. Everywhere Father Sounilhac went, people would ask about the holy shepherdess; it had reached a point where he was growing weary of the barrage of questions and inquiries directed at him. He began to wonder whether he should have ever exposed her incorrupt body in the first place, or brought it to Bishop de Marca's attention. Maybe he should have waited. He quickly dismissed these obtrusive thoughts, knowing full well that it was his moral duty as a priest to report such mysterious events to his superior.

He called his secretary, Monsieur Déprés, into his office to dictate a letter; he had decided that perhaps sending a reminder to the bishop would be enough to prompt His Excellency into making a decision on whether to further investigate or not.

"Monsieur Déprés," he called out loudly, "could you please come for a dictation?"

Antoine Déprés entered promptly and sat down in front of Father Sounilhac's wooden desk, fountain pen and ink bottle in hand. He placed them both on the edge of desk while he removed two blank pages from a folder. Antoine Déprés was organized and precise; he spoke very little, but knew exactly all the writing protocols that were regularly relied on in a parish office. Father Sounilhac depended heavily on his professionalism and discretion.

"Monsieur Déprés, please address this letter to Bishop Pierre de Marca of the Diocese of Toulouse." Father Sounilhac remained pensive for a moment, as he looked out of the office window. He cleared his throat, and began the dictation.

"My dear Excellency, I pray this letter finds you in good health and spirits. My letter is in follow-up to our communication from three months ago regarding the young shepherdess from Pibrac. I am curious as to whether you are considering a commission to investigate her cause for beatification? I am also hoping that a favorable decision to expose her body in the sanctuary will be forthcoming, as parishioners and citizens of Pibrac are all anxious to begin venerating this holy French shepherdess. If you are in need of any further details concerning the discovery of her remains, please do not hesitate to contact me at your earliest convenience. Your servant in Christ: Father Sounilhac." He paused again for a moment, wondering if he'd omitted anything important. "Monsieur Déprés, I will sign it, if you could take care of sending it promptly."

"Oui, mon père," responded Antoine Déprés with assurance. He quickly got up and left the office, discreetly closing the office door behind him.

Sixteen years later, on the 22nd of September, 1661, the Archbishop of Toulouse, Pierre de Marca, was buried under mounds of paperwork, his schedule interspersed with several parish confirmation visits, not to mention the extensive hours dedicated to diligently supervising the major seminary of Toulouse. Spring was most certainly his busiest season. He glanced at his schedule for the next month as he sat on the armchair by his reading desk. He had so many conflicts in his scheduled that he realized he would not be able to attend all of the diocesan visits in addition to the many confirmations that appeared on the schedule. He summoned Father Jean Dufour, whose office was in the next room. Father Dufour was a venerable and pious priest, simple and modest, a tower of virtue in the way that he lived and worked. He was archdeacon of the metropolitan church as well as vicar-general of the Archbishop of Toulouse.

"Father Dufour, I need to consult with you. If you can, please come to my office," Bishop de Marca called out across the room.

"How can I be of service, Your Excellency?" the priest replied calmly and thoughtfully as he entered the archbishop's office.

"I must admit, the schedule for this month is overwhelming!" replied the archbishop. "I must give priority to attending the confirmations, but I will need some help with the diocesan visits."

He decided that sending his trusted archdeacon, Jean Dufour, to conduct many of the parish pastoral visits, would help diminish the burden of his demanding schedule. The archbishop continued, "I was looking through the list, and I believe that sending you down to Pibrac, Colomier, Cornebarrieu, Léguevin, Launaguet, and Saint-Jean, over the next two to three weeks, will greatly unburden my schedule. Does this seem like a reasonable itinerary?" the prelate inquired.

"I think this assignment will work," replied Dufour, who was always willing and eager to assist the archbishop.

In quietly reviewing the assigned visits in his office, Father Dufour decided that a review of St. Mary Magdalene's parish in Pibrac was the ideal location to begin his rounds. *The parish barely contains two hundred souls, and would be quick to review,* he thought. He certainly did not want to start the diocesan visits with a troubled parish.

The archdeacon arrived without pomp and ceremony, which was what the vicar-general preferred when it came to diocesan pastoral visits. His arrival, however, at the rectory of St. Mary Magdalene's Church, was unexpected, as the diocesan letter, announcing the visit, had not yet arrived by mail. The shock upon opening the door and facing the archdeacon was distressing to Father Sounilhac, who had no foreknowledge of the visit, and so had not instructed the housekeeper to prepare a meal or ready a room, as was the custom for visits by prelates.

"Vicar-General, you are here! I mean, your arrival is a surprise! I mean, sudden!" the pastor blurted out without thinking, dumbfounded by such a high-profile visit.

"Yes, I am here to discuss the management of the parish, on behalf of Archbishop de Marca," the archdeacon declared to legitimize his arrival. The two stood at the entry, the door wide open, and looked at each other for what seemed an eternity.

Finally, as if to recover from his initial awkwardness, Father Sounilhac promptly engaged the prelate. "Do come in out of the cool evening night, Archdeacon, and please come and sit down in the parlor."

"Yes, thank you, that would delightful," Father Dufour said with poise, his usual serious demeanor clearly unfazed by the pastor's uneasiness. He continued, "If I am to assist the bishop in making those critical diocesan decisions, then I must get a firsthand view of the different parishes, you understand" insisted the Archdeacon who had felt Sounilhac's surprise and concern the moment he opened the door.

"Of course, Vicar-General, I would have, however, expected a letter announcing your arrival, since your business is of utmost importance," answered Father Sounilhac.

"One was indeed sent, but I am afraid it did not reach you on time," replied Father Dufour who was beginning to understand the pastor's anxious behavior.

"Is there anything I could get you before Madame de Sablonnières, the housekeeper, escorts you to your room?" the pastor inquired.

"Thank you, Father Sounilhac, I require nothing at the moment," answered the vicar-general, who was all too willing to proceed with his inquiry.

"Well, then," exclaimed the pastor. "How would you like to proceed with this review?"

"I think it wise and logical to begin with a tour of the church."

"So shall it be," Sounilhac replied, as he began to lead the archdeacon out of the parlor.

"Excuse me, Father, but is there a place I could put my bag before I begin with the tour of the church?" the archdeacon asked.

"Yes, of course, I will have Madame de Sablonnières take your bags to your room, with your permission," replied Father Sounilhac.

"That would be perfectly fine, and again, thank you for accommodating me on such short notice, Father Sounilhac," the vicar-general responded with sincerity.

As the archdeacon proceeded to exit the parlor to wait for the guided walk-around, Sounilhac called Madame de Sablonnières with a nervous and uneasy intonation. "Madame Sablonnières! Madame Sablonnières!"

Jehanne Sablonnières was a rotund, middle-aged woman, who was always busy managing either the business of the parish office or the cleaning and organizing of the presbytery.

"Oui, mon père, what can I do to help you?" responded the housekeeper.

Father Sounilhac, moving in close to the housekeeper's ear, whispered with some level of trepidation in his voice, "The vicar-general has arrived by surprise. I had no idea he was coming. Please fix a meal as quickly as you can, and prepare the guest bedroom to accommodate him. He has travelled a long distance to get here, and I am sure he is hungry. Can you do that?"

"Yes, Father, I will prepare something promptly," Jehanne Sablonnières responded with the most reassuring tone she could muster. Quickly, she fled into the kitchen, and went to work.

Reassured by his housekeeper's sense of urgency, Father Sounilhac proceeded to the hallway right next to the parlor, where he spoke with the vicar-general about general business issues. He then began the tour of the church, starting with the vestibule, followed by the sanctuary, and ending with the sacristy. It was in the sacristy, however, that the vicar-general's interest was piqued by Germaine Cousin's lead coffin, lying atop a brick mausoleum.

"What do we have here?" inquired Dufour, who was unfamiliar with the shepherdess's story. It had already been close to seventeen years since the dramatic discovery of her incorrupt remains, and Bishop de Marca had insisted on letting the drama subside quietly, without intervening, before taking any action.

"These are the incorrupt remains of a simple and perhaps holy shepherdess, Germaine Cousin, who died back in the summer of 1601," explained Father Sounilhac. After a brief reflective pause, he attempted to clarify, "I did write Bishop de Marca about the discovery, but have not heard back from him. I did not wish to push the matter any further, despite the constant persistence of the parishioners to venerate her and pray to her."

"It is a good thing that you hid her remains away until the Church did some investigation. I applaud your decision," the vicar-general reassured the pastor. He then added, "Father Sounilhac, I understand fully that the parishioners are attracted to the supernatural; this is normal and to be expected, but the goal here is not to create a circus in Pibrac but true devotion. I do believe this reflects Bishop de Marca's main concern." Pausing for a moment, he added, "But why hide her remains in the sacristy?"

"Father Dufour, I knew of no other appropriate location to put the body," replied Father Sounilhac. "Allow me to show you the shepherdess's body, if I may. Perhaps, then, would you be prompted to speak to the archbishop about initiating an investigation?" the pastor proposed. "In the interim, I am hoping that you will give permission for her body to be exposed, if only to incite religious fervor."

As Father Sounilhac moved to the side of the lead coffin, he slowly removed the top with the help of the archdeacon. The vicar-general's eyes opened wide in amazement; he had never seen an incorrupt corpse before. "Why, she is perfectly preserved, as if she had died this morning," the archdeacon uttered. He knelt in prayer before the coffin, touched by the mystical beauty of what he was seeing.

"O my Lord and my God!" Father Dufour let out in an almost imperceptible utterance. "How Jesus leaves us, at times, sweet signs from heaven."

He stood there, staring at the coffin for a long time, his face, wrinkled and weathered, immersed in deep thought. Suddenly, as if some profound understanding had been given him, he turned to Father Sounilhac. "Let not these remains ever be exposed again for public veneration, and let her corpse not move from the sacristy. It must be kept away from public view, until the Lord makes clear the holiness of this shepherdess. I will, however, allow prayerful offerings to heaven from the faithful to be done through Germaine's intercession. This I command you under threat of excommunication. Have I made myself clear, Father Sounilhac?" the vicar-general inquired with unnerving clarity.

Dumbfounded by the vicar-general's order, and the severity of his voice, he responded with astonishment, "Yes, Archdeacon, I will abide by your instructions. But I fail to understand the purpose of keeping her hidden."

"An investigation must be done first, Father Sounilhac," said the vicar-general. "Otherwise, increased religious fervor could do terrible damage to the integrity and credibility of the Church, should the miracles linked to her intercession be proven false. This, my dear Father Sounilhac, must be avoided at all costs."

"I understand fully."

"I am glad to hear that. And so, before I continue my diocesan tour, I think it imperative to see where, in the church, the shepherdess was discovered."

The pastor gladly escorted the vicar-general to the church, and once there, pointed out exactly where, beneath the flagstone, Germaine's corpse had been discovered.

"Once we located her body, we exhumed it immediately, as we needed to promptly entomb Madame Endoualle, who had already been dead for three days," explained the pastor. "The space in front of the ambo had already been reserved and purchased by the Endoualle family, a year or two before her death. I recall that it was embarrassing, to say the least, to find another inhumed corpse in the exact location where we intended to bury Madame Endoualle's remains. There was no record of Germaine Cousin being buried in that location. I was horrified when the corpse was found."

"I gather the remains of Madame Endoualle are still interred in the same place, here before the ambo?" asked Father Dufour pensively.

"Why, yes they are," replied Sounilhac. "Why do you ask?"

"I would like you to dig up her remains," ordered the archdeacon.

"Right now?" inquired Sounilhac, verifying that he had heard correctly.

"Why, yes, my dear pastor, immediately. There is no sense postponing this inevitable step in the inquiry," Dufour added.

"But Archdeacon…" was all Soulnihac could utter before the Father Dufour cut him off, saying, "No buts, my dear brother in Christ. The first question in the inquiry will have to do with whether the soil was amenable to minimizing the corruption of a corpse. If indeed Madame Endoualle is found to be decomposed, then the issue of Germaine's preservation could be put forth to the commission as miraculous."

Suddenly, Father Sounilhac's behavior took on a zeal that the archdeacon had not yet seen in him. "I will summon two workers to dig up the remains," the pastor called out as he ran off to the parish office, leaving the archdeacon behind. It took no less than two hours for Guillaume Cassé and Gaillard Baron, the two workmen usually hired by the church for digging graves, to arrive at the parish, ready to dig up some flagstone and dirt. They had remembered how, years ago, they had discovered the incorrupt body of Germaine Cousin in the very spot they were preparing to dig. There was a sense of mystery in this exhumation that intrigued both workers.

Once Archdeacon Dufour gave the order, the two workmen began to lift the flagstone and shovel the dirt that covered Madame Endoualle's coffin. It took twenty minutes of hard labor to finally exhume the coffin. They placed it at the feet of the archdeacon, who immediately ordered it opened. The stench was overpowering, though the rotting phase had long ceased. There is a smell associated with death, and it lingers for a long time, even though a corpse may have thoroughly been decomposed. Hands over their faces to keep from being overtaken both by the smell and the frightful sight of death, the archdeacon and pastor walked away promptly, saying to the two workers, as they were exiting the church, "Seal the coffin and return it to the ground. Bury it and speak of it to nobody. Is this clear?"

"Yes, Father, we will do as you say," the two workers responded, understanding that they were taking an oath that could not be broken.

In Jean Dufour's mind, it was clear that the incorrupt remains of Germaine Cousin were indeed in the realm of the miraculous.

Bishop de Marca frequently glanced at the report he received from Father Sounilhac several years ago; it layed opened on the small reading desk by his armchair. In it, Father Sounilhac described in great details the events surrounding the discovery of Germaine Cousin's remains seventeen years earlier. He pondered how he should approach the numerous problems associated with such a discovery. He received no real, strong answer to his prayers. In any event, when could he ever find time to concentrate on this matter? He had parish visits, confirmations, ordinations, and it seemed the list of events just went on. His Excellency rose from behind the papers stacked on his desk and walked over to the window to admire the young birds dutifully making their nests. Spring had arrived early, and the newness of the season refreshed the bishop's spirit. He thought, *Is it not interesting how the birds know exactly what has to be done; there is no sense of them being overwhelmed. They focus on the essentials; they complete what God, in His design, foresaw as needing to be completed in time and in season. The order is remarkable, and events unfold according to His will.*

He reached for the envelopes that had been brought in by his secretary that morning and placed them on his desk. As he glanced at the first letter atop the pile, he recognized the archdeacon's seal.

I wonder what urgent report Father Dufour had to write this early in his diocesan visits? he asked himself. He proceeded to open the envelope and read it intently.

> Your Excellency, there is a great deal of evidence supporting my recommendation that you open an investigation for the cause of Germaine Cousin of Pibrac. I suspect that an ecclesiastical tribunal would

have very little difficulty in declaring her venerable. You must consider seriously what I am telling you, dear Excellency. I should like you to see her incorrupt remains, as I have, during the course of my diocesan visit to Pibrac, before moving forward. If my preliminary investigation is reliable, it should not take long before you can begin the investigation.

Bishop de Marca put the letter down on his desk, and paused for an instant before calling his secretary for a dictation. He wanted to meet both with Fathers Dufour and Sounilhac within the week.

Sitting in the bishop's office, fathers Dufour and Sounilhac listened intently to his Excellency's arguments for not rushing forward with any kind of investigation regarding Pibrac's shepherdess. "Do remember, Father Sounilhac and Archdeacon Dufour, that the Church always moves cautiously in these matters. Furthermore, I will reflect awhile longer about advancing her cause. On whether to display her body in the church, I concur with Father Dufour that the body of Germaine Cousin must be hidden from sight until further notice.

"Thank you, Your Excellency. I will be obedient to the Church's decision," Father Sounilhac replied.

EPILOGUE

Historical records from the diocese of Toulouse confirm that Germaine's incorrupt body remained hidden from public view, in the sacristy of St. Mary Magdalene's Church in Pibrac, between 1645 and 1793. Despite the lead coffin being confined to the sacristy, the public still prayed to Germaine for intercessory prayers to Jesus for miracles. And indeed, numerous cures totaling four hundred, including healings and wonders of all sorts, were recorded right up until she was declared blessed by Pope Pius IX, on May 7th, 1864. More miracles were again documented for her canonization on June 29th, 1867, which was pronounced again by Pope Pius IX. Germaine's remains are, still today, venerated by thousands of pilgrims at a shrine located in the heart of Pibrac, France.

It is intriguing that her canonization took place close to two hundred years after her cause had been considered worthy of an investigation. Perhaps the good Lord felt it best to keep her life hidden until the nineteenth century, knowing full well that prior to that time few would be capable of understanding the Lord's tolerance of this kind of suffering in youth. Still, even today, the story of Germaine elicits more anger than it does tears of pity and sympathy; anger in the direction of the father and stepmother who perpetrated the abuses, but also rage directed at the priests who tolerated it. The great mystery of how the Lord draws those He loves to the cross, alongside His mother, is a subject of great revulsion for those who have not yet abandoned themselves completely to the Lord's perfect plan of salvation. But it remains a sign of great hope for those souls steeped in childlike humility, who trustingly, without commotion, clamor, or wailing, commit to follow Christ to Calvary, for His promises offer great comfort for those who persevere to the end. Father Jean Pierre de Caussade, an eighteenth-century Jesuit priest, writes well about the necessity to not intellectualize these great unknown mysteries surrounding human suffering. He writes,

> *It is God working in the soul to make it like unto Himself. Perfection is neither more nor less than the faithful co-operation of the soul with this work of God, and is begun, grows, and is consummated in the soul unperceived and in secret. The science of theology is full of theories and explanations of the wonders of this state in each soul according to its capacity. One may be conversant with all these speculations, speak and write about them admirably, instruct others and guide souls; yet, if these theories are only in the mind, one is, compared with those who, without any knowledge of these theories, receive the meaning of the designs of God and do His holy will, like a sick physician compared to simple people in perfect health.*

Indeed, this eighteenth-century spiritual director knew full well to tread carefully when trying to interpret the mysterious climb to Calvary. He goes on to write:

Speculation must be laid aside, and everything arranged by God as regards actions, and sufferings must be accepted with simplicity, for those things that happen at each moment by the divine command or permission are always the most holy, the best and the most divine for us.

It is by this meditation that we can lay to rest the true story of Cinderella. Germaine Cousin neither protested nor forsook her tormentors, in a way consistent with the Savior. For this reason, she was like a lamb, precious in the sight of the Lord; because, like Him, who preceded her, she was oppressed and was afflicted, "yet He did not open His mouth; like a lamb that is led to slaughter, and like a sheep that is silent before its shearers, So He did not open His mouth" (Isaiah 53:7, NASB).

AUTHOR'S NOTES

In writing this book, the author consulted the following writings of noteworthy authors to assist in the priests' homilies and spiritual counseling:

1. Sermon inspired from Fr Bede Jarrett OP 1934
2. The works of Francis de Sales (1567-1622): "Introduction to the devout life."
3. The writings of Father Dajczer (†2009)
4. Father Jean Pierre de Caussade S.J. (†1751), "Abandonment to Divine Providence" St. Louis, MO: Harper Book Co., 1921, 282 pp.
5. Servant of God Archbishop Luis Maria Martinez "The Fire of the Holy Spirit (†1956)
6. Father John Grou's, "Manual for Interior Souls." London: St. Anselm's Society, 1905